HISTOLOGY

AND EMBRYOLOGY

GERRIT BEVELANDER, A.B., M.A., Ph.D.

Professor of Histology, University of Texas,
Dental Branch and The Graduate School of Biomedical Sciences,
Houston, Texas

141 Illustrations

HENRY KIMPTON *London, 1967*

PREFACE

THE main purpose of this atlas is to present the subject of oral histology and embryology in a clear, concise, and systematic fashion and thus permit the mastery of this topic with a minimum of time and effort.

The illustrations were prepared from my personal collection of material accumulated over the past several years. The descriptive text is based on a study of the specimens illustrated and is designed to emphasize the pertinent features of each preparation.

The first section is devoted to the early development and histogenesis of the tooth. Following this, the various parts of the tooth and adnexa are arranged as follows: dentin, enamel, pulp, cementum, periodontal membrane, alveolus, gingivae, eruption, palate, mucous membranes, and finally the temporomandibular joint.

It will be noted that an attempt has been made to relate practical applications which appear to be relevant. In addition to development and normal structure, changes occurring as the result of aging—so-called retrogressive changes—are described and illustrated in many instances. This important aspect of oral histology of which the student should be aware is not usually treated in current texts.

A unique feature of the atlas is the inclusion of several electron micrographs illustrating the morphologic features of dental tissues in detail. The inclusion of these micrographs affords an insight into many aspects of structure not heretofore readily available.

I would like to express my appreciation to Professor Hiroshi Nakahara for his valuable assistance in the preparation of the illustrations, and also to Professor Harold S. Skjonsby for his critical reading and constructive suggestions relating to the text material.

GERRIT BEVELANDER
Houston, Texas

V

CONTENTS

ATLAS OF ORAL HISTOLOGY AND EMBRYOLOGY

1 EMBRYOLOGY and EARLY HISTOGENESIS

Figure 1. In the human embryo the dental anlagen develop at approximately six weeks of intra-uterine life. These structures are known as the dental lamina and consist of a proliferation of oral epithelium which extends into the underlying mesenchyme. They are present in both jaws and have a U-shaped configuration. They are known as the dental lamina.

The embryonic face of approximately six weeks observed in a frontal section presents the appearance shown here. Of particular interest are the dental laminae which appear as bilateral structures in each jaw. It should be recalled that the laminae are continuous and appear on either side of the jaw owing to the fact that the face has been sectioned, as mentioned before. It is from these structures, the dental laminae, that the future tooth germs develop.

Other features of interest in this photograph are the structure and relations of the nasal cavity, which at this juncture is continuous with the oral cavity and the position of the lateral palatal processes which give rise to the bulk of the palate. Also shown is Meckel's cartilage which serves as a temporary support for this part of the developing mandible.

2

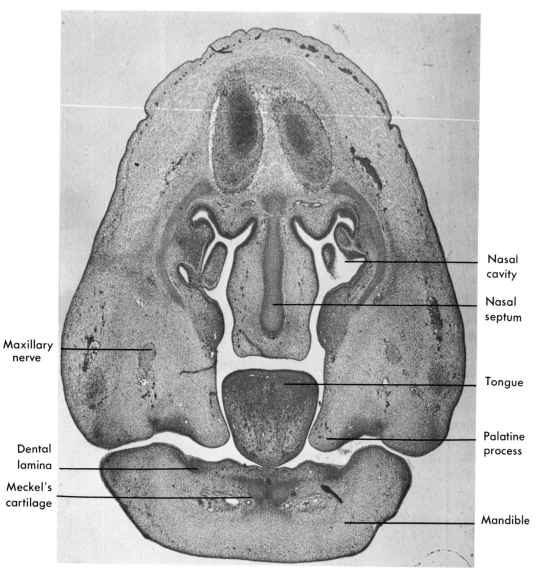

Nasal
cavity

Nasal
septum

Maxillary
nerve

Tongue

Dental
lamina

Palatine
process

Meckel's
cartilage

Mandible

Figure 1. Section of head of 28 mm embryo (pig). ×24.

Figure 2. This sectional view of the dental anlage shows the proliferation of the oral epithelium of both the basal layer and the superficial cells. Active cell division occurs at this stage of development which results in the configuration known as the dental lamina. Note also that the dental lamina is migrating into the underlying mesenchyme.

Figure 3. The state of development just described is not retained for any considerable time. As in other parts of the growing embryo, differentiation and change in size and configuration occur continuously. Once the dental lamina is established, a series of subsequent events occurs. The first of these is in association with further growth and differentiation of the dental lamina, a split in this structure which gives rise to a labial proliferation known as the labial lamina or lip band furrow. This structure is associated with the later formation of the vestibule. Also shown is a change in the dental anlage, which has now differentiated into a ball of cells known as the tooth bud or germ.

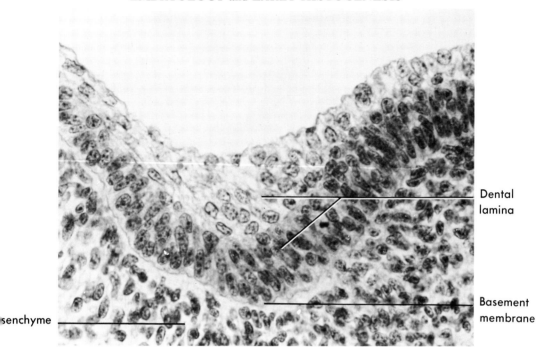

Dental
lamina

Basement
membrane

senchyme

Figure 2. Dental lamina. × 640.

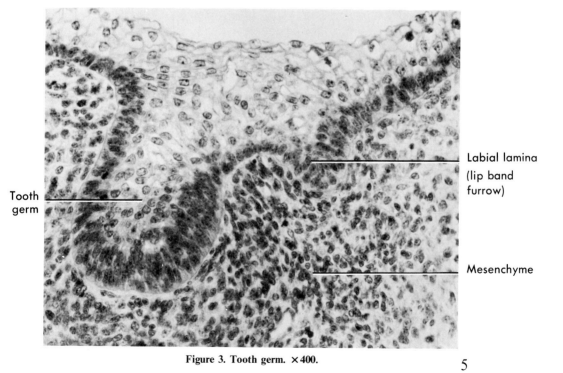

Tooth
germ

Labial lamina
(lip band
furrow)

Mesenchyme

Figure 3. Tooth germ. × 400.

5

Figure 4. In each developing jaw one may distinguish between the dental lamina, extending throughout the arch of each jaw, and the tooth germs which arise as a group of differentiating and proliferating cells at the site of the future deciduous teeth. The tooth germs appear as solid rounded structures somewhat separated from the dental lamina. Soon after this stage of development has been attained, a further differentiation of the tooth germ occurs giving rise to the stage of development known as the early enamel organ. When this state has been reached (shown here at about the tenth week), the developing tooth germ consists of a ball-shaped structure indented at its base. It is subtended by the dental lamina which is now becoming reduced in size. The outer limits of the early enamel organ are derived from the basal layer of the oral epithelium, the inner portion from the superficial layers.

Figure 5. In a somewhat later stage in the development of this structure, a further differentiation and change in configuration has taken place. This is due to the invasion of the mesenchyme at the base of the enamel organ, to growth, and to further differentiation of the cellular components which make up the embryonic tooth.

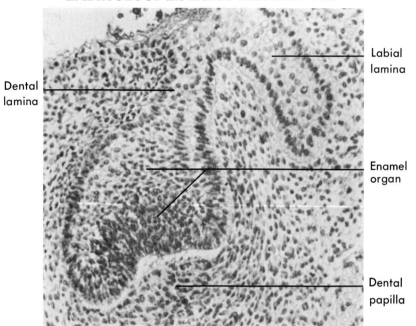

Dental
lamina

Labial
lamina

Enamel
organ

Dental
papilla

Figure 4. Early enamel organ. × 240.

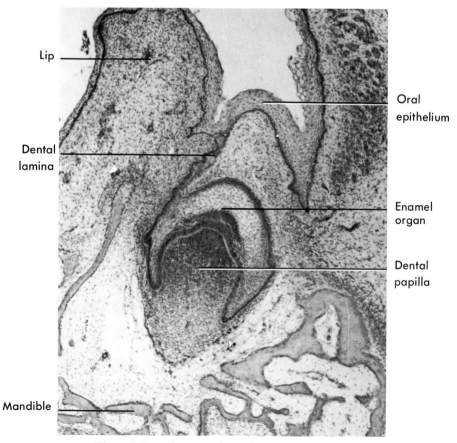

Lip

Dental
lamina

Mandible

Oral
epithelium

Enamel
organ

Dental
papilla

Figure 5. Enamel organ and associated structures. × 40.

Figure 6. Thus far we have been concerned with the early stage of tooth development up to and including development of the early enamel organ. During this time, many other important changes have been occurring in the overall growth and development of the entire face. Some of these changes are illustrated here.

One of the most obvious differences in the face is the increase in size. Also shown in the photograph is the change in the configuration of the nasal and oral cavities, attributable in part to the growth of the palatal anlage. This results in the midline fusion of the hard palate thus separating the nasal and oral cavities, the palate serving as the floor of the former and the roof of the latter. One may also observe the increase in the size of the tongue and the depression of this structure in the oral cavity. Many of the bones of the face have begun to form and mineralize; glands, muscles, and nerves are also readily observed even at this low magnification. Finally, attention is called to the two bilaterally placed enamel organs in each jaw, showing their position in relation to other associated structures.

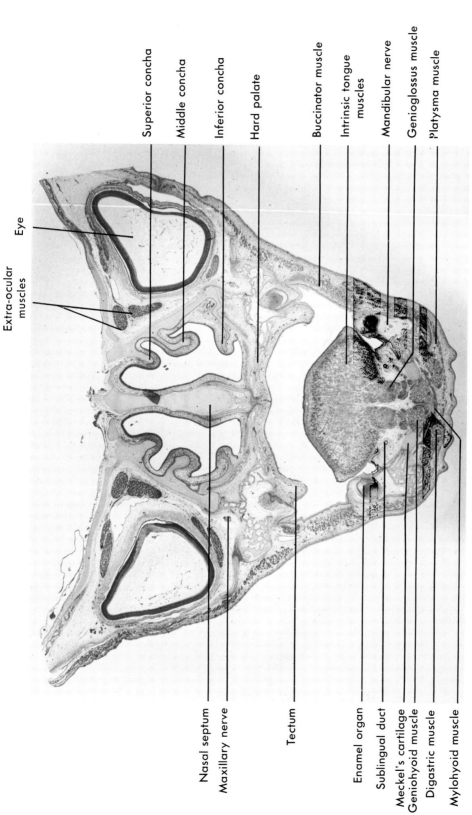

Extra-ocular
muscles

Eye

Superior concha

Middle concha

Inferior concha

Hard palate

Buccinator muscle

Intrinsic tongue
muscles

Mandibular nerve

Genioglossus muscle

Platysma muscle

Nasal septum

Maxillary nerve

Tectum

Enamel organ

Sublingual duct

Meckel's cartilage

Geniohyoid muscle

Digastric muscle

Mylohyoid muscle

Figure 6. Section of head of 3 month embryo. ×11.

2

Figure 7. At approximately three months of intra-uterine development the embryonic tooth has reached the state of development shown here. This structure, the enamel organ, has undergone several changes during its development and now consists of the following: The shape of the enamel organ is roughly that of an inverted goblet. It is subtended by the ever decreasing epithelial strand, the dental lamina. It lies embedded in mesenchyme and occupies a position considerably below the oral epithelium.

The enamel organ consists of the following components: an external layer of cells extending from the junction of the dental lamina to the region of the invagination at the base of the enamel organ. This layer of cells is known as the outer enamel epithelium. Continuous with this layer and extending to the basal side of this structure marking the boundary of the future pulp cavity is the second cellular component, the inner enamel epithelium. These cells will later become the ameloblasts. Less clearly shown is an attenuated layer superimposed upon the inner enamel epithelium, a third component, the stratum intermedium. In some embryonic teeth there is also a temporary piling up of epithelial cells above the inner enamel epithelium. These cells are collectively known as the enamel knot. Enclosed within the confines of the sac-like enamel organ, whose boundaries consist of the inner and outer enamel epithelium, are a collection of loosely arranged stellate cells derived from the superficial layers of the oral epithelium. This collection of cells is known as the stellate reticulum or enamel pulp.

The enamel organ as shown in the photograph is subject to change in shape due in large part to the proliferation of mesenchymal cells at the base of the organ. These cells known as the dental papilla invade the enamel organ, changing the configuration considerably as will be shown in several of the subsequent illustrations.

10

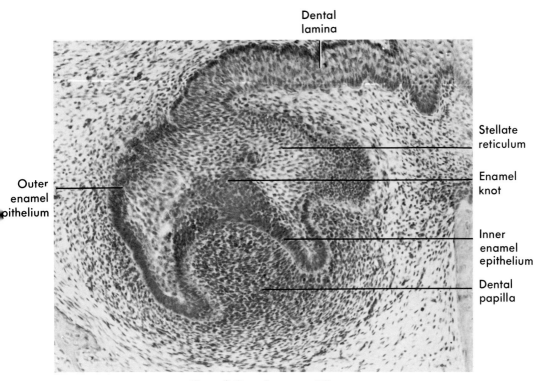

Dental
lamina

Stellate
reticulum

Enamel
knot

Inner
enamel
epithelium

Dental
papilla

Outer
enamel
epithelium

Figure 7. Enamel organ. × 160.

11

Figure 8. The continued growth and differentiation that occur following the state described as the enamel organ consist of the following events: The mesenchymal cells of the dental papilla proliferate and invade the enamel organ. This stage of development is reached at approximately six months of intra-uterine development (120 mm embryo). Other changes that may be observed consist of:

1. The cells on the periphery of the embryonic pulp cavity differentiate, first in the coronal region, to become odontoblasts.

2. A similar differentiation of the outer epithelium occurs giving rise to tall columnar cells, the ameloblasts.

3. The union of the four cellular components of the enamel organ at the coronal part of the developing tooth. These combined layers are known as the combined or (reduced) enamel epithelium.

4. Following the changes just described the next important event that takes place is the formation of dentin. Before this occurs a collection of reticular fibers derived from the pulp (Korff's fibers) penetrate between the odontoblasts to the region where the opposing odontoblasts and ameloblasts meet. These fibers lie in a space on the pulpal side of the dentino-enamel junction containing tissue fluid and sulphated mucopolysaccharides.

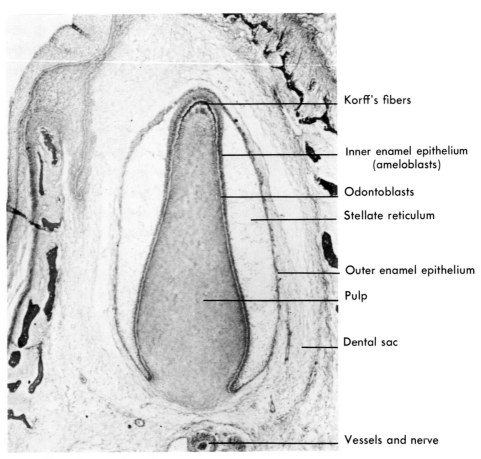

Korff's fibers

Inner enamel epithelium
(ameloblasts)

Odontoblasts

Stellate reticulum

Outer enamel epithelium

Pulp

Dental sac

Vessels and nerve

Figure 8. Developing incisor showing Korff's fibers. ×40.

Figure 9. The previous photograph shows at relatively low magnification some of the most important features of the tooth which are present just before mineralization of dentin and enamel occur. Shown here in greater detail is the origin of Korff's fibers, which at this stage of development arise from the pulp subjacent to the odontoblasts. Shown also are the position of the odontoblasts relative to the ameloblasts and also the appearance and distribution of Korff's fibers. These fibers form part of the dentinal matrix. The specimens illustrated in Figures 8 and 9 were prepared by a method (Foote-Hortega) specially designed to bring out the fibers, hence cellular structures are not clearly defined.

Dentino-
enamel
junction

Ameloblast
nuclei

Korff's fibers

Odontoblast
nuclei

Reticular
fibers
in pulp

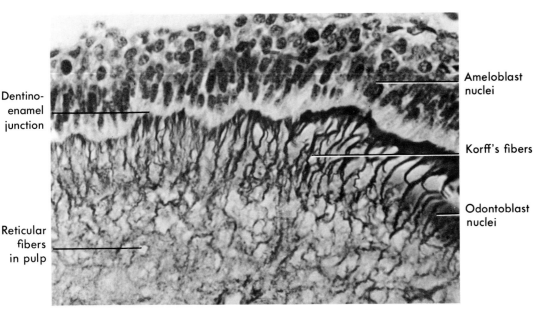

Figure 9. Detail of development of Korff's fibers. ×640.

Figure 10. The state of development is illustrated at relatively high magnification of the two groups of cells responsible for the formation of dentin and enamel respectively just before mineralization occurs. The details shown in this photograph cannot be brought out by the silver methods used to prepare the specimens shown in Figures 8 and 9. Examination of this figure shows on the right the incompletely differentiated ameloblasts with their nuclei more or less centrally located in the cell. These cells are in intimate contact with an adjacent group of cells also incompletely differentiated, some still dividing with basally placed nuclei. It is obvious that at this stage of development the odontoblasts and the ameloblasts are in intimate contact. The point of contact between these cells is subsequently known as the dentino-enamel junction. It should be noted that the section illustrated here was stained with aniline dyes which do not show reticular fibers. In order to understand and visualize the structural components present in the region of the odontoblasts it is necessary to superimpose the structure shown in Figure 9 upon those shown in this figure.

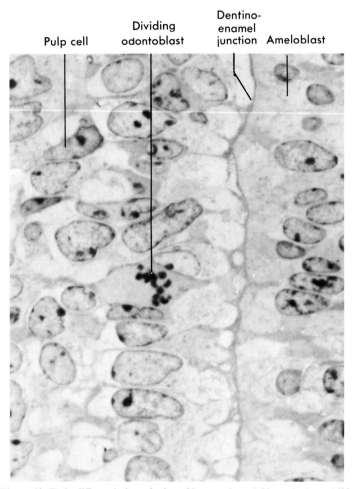

Figure 10. Early differentiation of odontoblasts and ameloblasts (rat). × 1600.

Figure 11. The electron micrograph illustrates in detail several features not shown in the light level photomicrographs. The dentino-enamel junction, *d.e.j.,* is shown. In the lower region of the odontoblast two varieties of cellular organelles are abundant, namely, the rough endoplasmic reticulum, *e.r.,* and a profusion of polyribosomes, *r.,* scattered throughout the entire cell. Also of interest is the terminal part of the cell divided into finger-like projections, the future odontoblast processes. These latter structures occupy a position in the predentin area or space, *p.d.a.* Also shown in this space are the delicate Korff fibers, *k,* embedded in the fluid ground substance. This micrograph illustrates the state of development of the odontoblast before mineralization occurs. Its chief characteristic is the presence of the rough endoplasmic reticulum and the numerous polyribosomes indicative of a cell synthesizing protein.

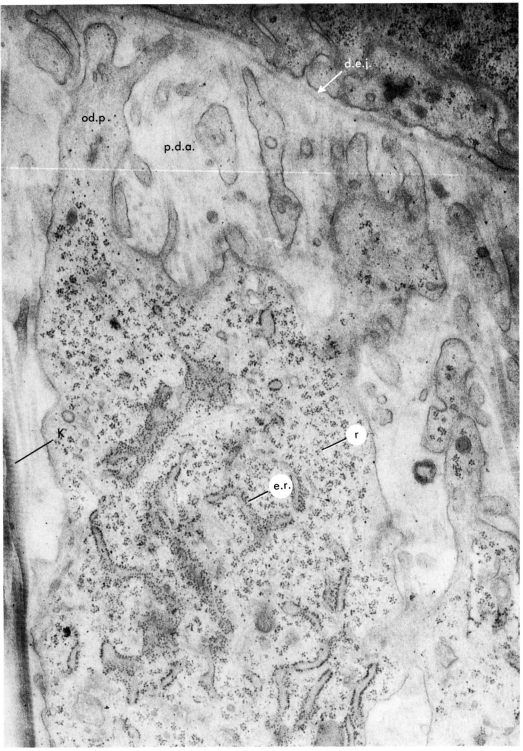

Figure 11. Electron micrograph of an odontoblast (rat incisor). ×27,000. (From Bevelander, G., and Nakahara, H.: Formation and mineralization of dentin. Anat. Rec., *156*:303, 1966.)

Figure 12. This electron micrograph shows early formation of dentin in the rat incisor and the distribution of Korff's fibers in relation to the odontoblast, *od.*, and the pre-dentin space, *p.d.s.*, in a stage of development somewhat more advanced than the cell illustrated in Figure 11. Examination of the cytoplasm of the cell shows again the prominent rough endoplasmic reticulum, *e.r.*, and the profusion of polyribosomes, *r.* The difference in the state of development shown in this micrograph consists chiefly in the increase in size of the pre-dentin space and also the presence of the prominent fibers, *K,* (Korff's fibers), which arise from the pulp, pass between the odontoblasts, and terminate in the region of dentino-enamel junction, *d.e.j.*

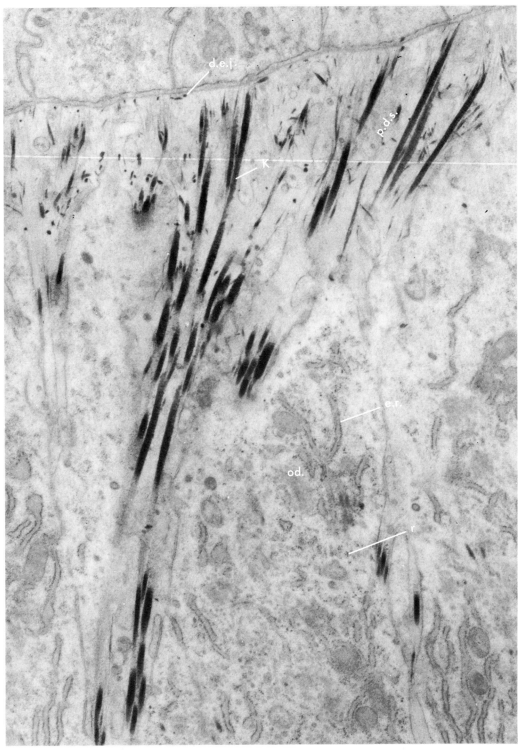

Figure 12. Electron micrograph showing early dentin formation. ×15,000. (From Bevelander, G., and Nakahara, H.: Formation and mineralization of dentin. Anat. Rec., *156*:303, 1966.)

2 DENTOGENESIS and AMELOGENESIS

Figure 13. Until this juncture we have been considering the changes that take place in the developing tooth before mineralization of dentin and enamel occurs. At approximately six months the developing central teeth have reached the state shown here in a decalcified section of a lower incisor from a 120 mm pig embryo. Examination of the coronal part of this tooth shows that the four layers of the enamel organ have been compressed to form the combined enamel epithelium. The inner layer of this group of tissues consists of functional ameloblasts and directly pulpward one may observe a thin increment of enamel. Facing the enamel is a wider increment of dentin and deep to this tissue are the odontoblasts located on the periphery of the pulp. The pulp now occupies a considerable area and is already vascularized and innervated. Examination of this figure makes it apparent that the mineralization occurs first in the coronal region. The first tissue to mineralize is dentin. In addition to the changes that have taken place in the tooth itself, changes in the surrounding structures are also of interest.

We observe that the coronal aspect of the tooth now lies in close apposition to the oral mucosa. The dental lamina is much reduced in size and a new structure not heretofore mentioned has developed from it, namely, the permanent tooth germ anlage. The entire developing tooth lies enclosed within a fibrous membrane, which is the outer limit of the dental sac within which the tooth develops. Finally the bony crypt, the future jaw and alveolus, has already reached a fairly high degree of development. For explanations of labels (1), (2), and (3), see pp. 25, 27, and 33 respectively.

22

DENTOGENESIS and AMELOGENESIS

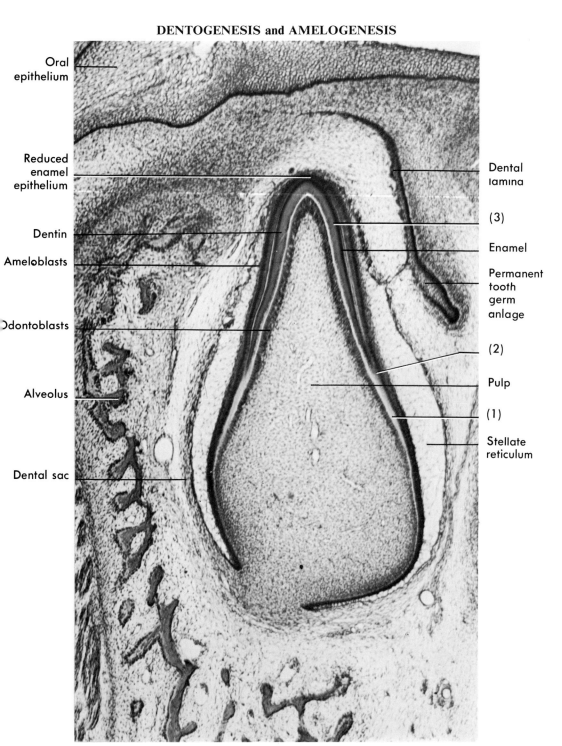

Oral epithelium

Reduced enamel epithelium

Dentin

Ameloblasts

Odontoblasts

Alveolus

Dental sac

Dental lamina

(3)

Enamel

Permanent tooth germ anlage

(2)

Pulp

(1)

Stellate reticulum

Figure 13. Early mineralization in developing tooth (pig). ×60.

Figure 14. The developing tooth in which mineralization of dentin and enamel have been initiated is illustrated in Figure 13. Some of the features of the embryonic tooth at this stage of development were briefly described. It was indicated in the previous paragraphs that various parts of a developing tooth are in diverse states of development. Accordingly, a detailed study of such an embryonic tooth is instructive in an attempt to understand the mechanism of tooth development and the subsequent structure of the various parts of the tooth and its supporting adnexa.

Three different areas or levels of the tooth illustrated in Figure 13 will be described here in greater detail. The first level, indicated by (1) in Figure 13 and shown here at greater magnification, represents a strip beginning at the right of the pulp showing the undifferentiated odontoblasts exhibiting a terminal elongation, Tomes' dentinal process, and a wide light zone, the pre-dentin space. Immediately to the right is a zone of dense cells, the undifferentiated ameloblasts, and adjacent to them a layer of small polygonal cells, the stratum intermedium, is shown. External to these cells is the stellate reticulum, consisting of scattered stellate shaped cells lying in a ground substance rich in sulfated mucopolysaccharides. Not shown in this illustration is the externally situated outer enamel epithelium.

24

DENTOGENESIS and AMELOGENESIS

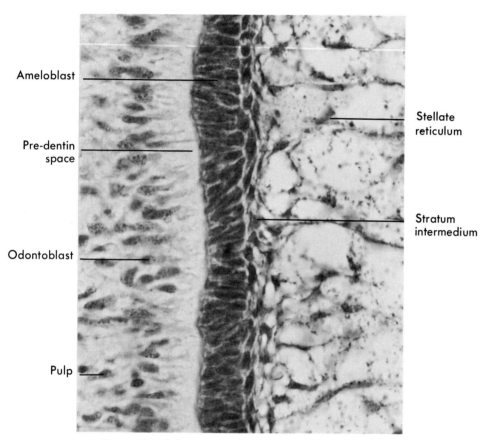

Ameloblast

Pre-dentin space

Odontoblast

Pulp

Stellate reticulum

Stratum intermedium

Figure 14. Cellular components of late enamel organ. ×640.

Figure 15. This illustrates a strip of the same tooth at the level indicated by (2) in Figure 13. This slightly more coronal region of this tooth shows several marked differences from the one first described in Figure 14. Beginning with the pulp to the extreme left, one may observe an increase in the size of the pulp cells, scattered delicate fibrils, and a relative increase in the area occupied by the intercellular ground substance.

Directing attention now to the odontoblasts, those at the bottom (apical) part of the strip are smaller than those at the top (coronal) part of the tooth. Tomes' dentinal processes are more highly developed and the odontoblasts have retreated from the distal surface of the ameloblasts leaving a well defined pre-dentin space. In addition, the beginning of mineralization of this latter space is also clearly shown. Examination of the photograph shows that at this optical level, initial mineralization occurs first in the region of the dentino-enamel junction as small droplets (calcoglobules). This process occurs first in the coronal region and continues in the apical direction until an increment of partially mineralized dentin is deposited. Mineralization occurs in rhythmic fashion. While mineralization of the first increment takes place, the odontoblasts continue to retreat in a pulpward direction, during which time Tomes' dentinal process elongates and an additional zone of pre-dentin is constantly made available for the succeeding increment of dentin to become mineralized. It can be observed further that although the ameloblasts are in this stage considerably elongated, enamel formation in this part of the tooth exhibiting mineralized dentin is not evident.

26

DENTOGENESIS and AMELOGENESIS

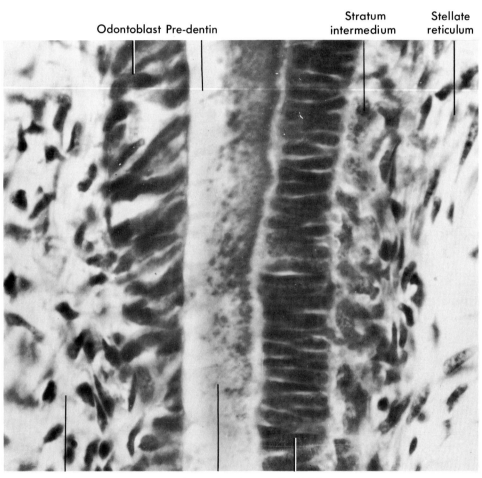

Odontoblast   Pre-dentin   Stratum intermedium   Stellate reticulum

Pulp   Mineralizing dentin   Ameloblast

Figure 15. Initiation of dentin mineralization. ×860.

Figure 16. This electron micrograph illustrates part of the dentinal matrix of a developing tooth in the region of the dentino-enamel junction and shows the profusion of Korff's fibers, *K*, scattered throughout the entire matrix, patches of granular material believed to be sulfated mucopolysaccharide, *m.p.*, and small isolated dark areas indicative of crystal formation, *m.c.* Mineralization apparently occurs first in isolated areas of mucopolysaccharide and subsequently or concomitantly on the collagen fibers.

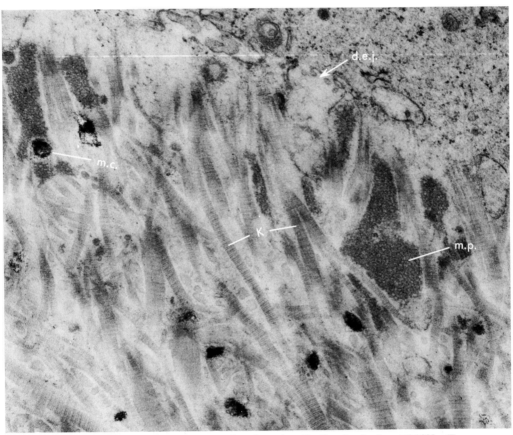

Figure 16. Electron micrograph illustrating the mineralization in dentin. ×36,000. (From Bevelander, G., and Nakahara, H.: Formation and mineralization of dentin. Anat. Rec., *156*:303, 1966.)

29

Figure 17. In the region of the dentino-enamel junction, *d.e.j.,* of the rat incisor, portions of odontoblasts, *o,* and ameloblasts, *a,* are seen here in the state of development prior to mineralization and to the formation of Tomes' processes in both kinds of cells. The cytoplasm of these cells exhibit an abundance of rough endoplasmic reticulum, *e.r.,* and ribosomes, *r.,* indicative of active protein synthesis.

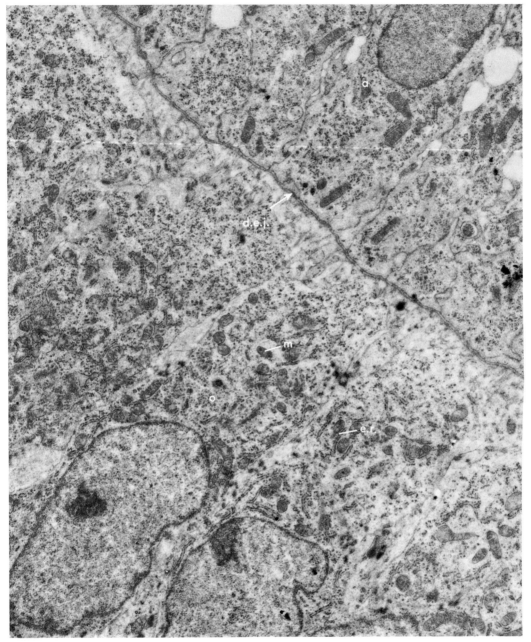

Figure 17. Electron micrograph showing early development of odontoblasts and ameloblasts. ×6400.

31

Figure 18. A strip of the tooth shown in Figure 13 at the level indicated by (3). Of particular interest in this photograph are the appearance of the odontoblasts, rather stout elongated cells, all in an active functional state, the prominent Tomes' dentinal processes extending throughout the entire width of the dentin, the prominent light (unmineralized) pre-dentin space, and to the right, a fairly wide increment of mineralized dentin.

Abutting on the dentin is a somewhat narrower zone stained darkly, which represents an increment of mineralized enamel. To the right of the enamel is shown a layer of extremely tall narrow cells, the functional ameloblasts. At the terminal surface of these cells slender protoplasmic processes extend throughout the entire width of the enamel. This photograph illustrates at the level of light microscopy a region of the tooth in which active elaboration and mineralization of dentin and enamel are simultaneously taking place.

DENTOGENESIS and AMELOGENESIS

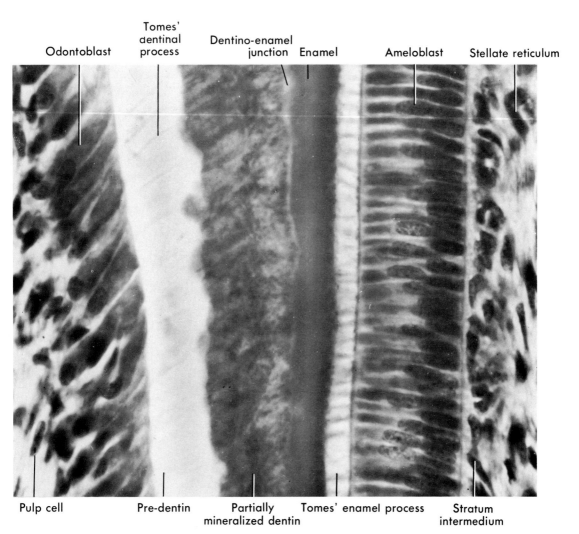

Odontoblast • Tomes' dentinal process • Dentino-enamel junction • Enamel • Ameloblast • Stellate reticulum

Pulp cell • Pre-dentin • Partially mineralized dentin • Tomes' enamel process • Stratum intermedium

Figure 18. Histogenesis of dentin and enamel. × 860.

33

Figure 19. This electron micrograph shows a region at the dentino-enamel junction at the time in development when enamel, *e,* is initially deposited. The ameloblasts, *a,* show fewer ribosomes and less endoplasmic reticulum than similar cells in the state of development before mineralization occurs. Tomes' processes are not well developed at this stage. The increment of enamel which is adjacent to the more highly mineralized dentin, *d,* appears as fine strands or fibers. The organic part of enamel, in which are embedded the elongated dark needle-shaped structures of incompletely developed crystals of hydroxyapatite, is eukeratin.

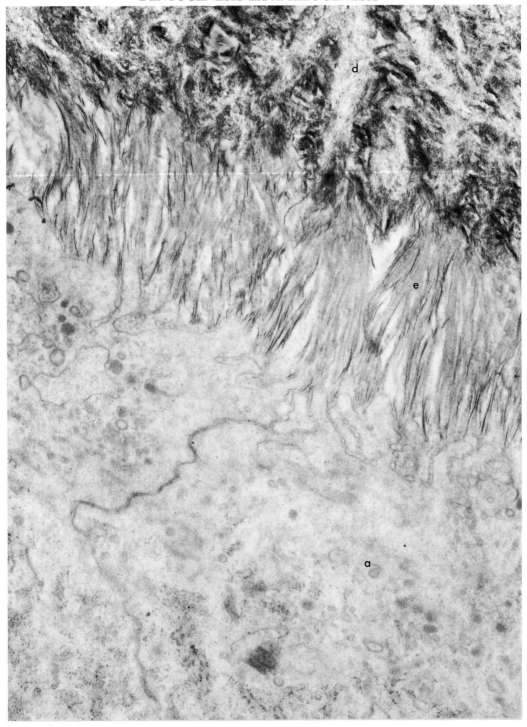

Figure 19. An electron micrograph showing early stage of mineralization of enamel. ×17,500.

Figure 20. An electron micrograph showing detail of a mature ameloblast obtained at the time mineralization was taking place (secreting stage). In this stage the mitochondria, *m,* are numerous, the endoplasmic reticulum, *e.r.,* is still prominent, and the Golgi apparatus, *G,* is also well shown. Lipid droplets, *L,* are present, but free ribosomes are no longer numerous. Also shown are the cell junction, *c.j.,* and the nucleus, *N.* The organelles of this active cell are in marked contrast with those shown in the cell in the premineralization state.

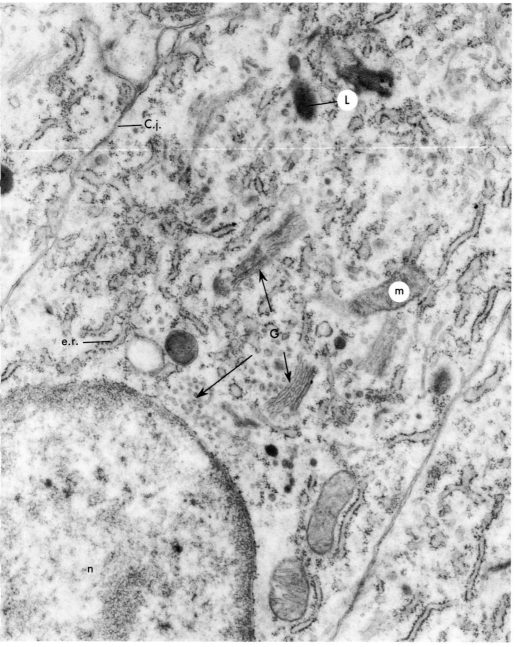

Figure 20. An electron micrograph of an ameloblast in active "secretory" phase. × 17,500.

Figure 21. Mineralization of dentin and enamel is preceded by a series of events which involves differentiation of certain cells, the elaboration of an organic complex in the case of dentin, the pre-dentin, and then a triggering mechanism which sets off the mineralizing process. This series of steps is repeated many times during the formation of the tooth. Although mineralization is a necessary part of this series of events, it is not the only one and it is important to bear in mind that the organic phase of mineralization, though less dramatic, is equally important. A part of a growing tooth is shown in which a considerable amount of mineralized dentin has been formed. During the course of tooth formation there is a repeated pattern of fiber formation and ground substance elaboration which must occur for completion of tooth formation. It will be recalled that fibers are an important component of the dentinal matrix.

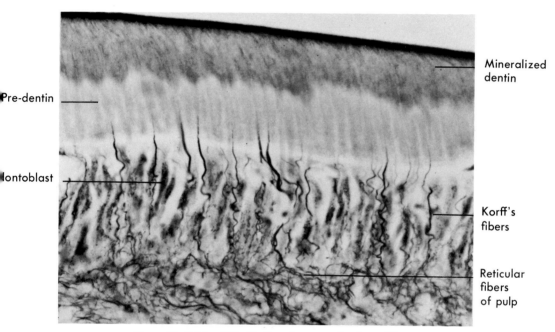

Mineralized
dentin

Pre-dentin

Odontoblast

Korff's
fibers

Reticular
fibers
of pulp

Figure 21. Origin of Korff's fibers in mature dentin. × 640.

Figure 22. When dentin is first deposited, it is only partially mineralized. This is difficult to ascertain from routine histologic sections. However, the fact that this is true makes more readily understandable the several modifications of a structural and chemical nature, which frequently occur in the mature tooth. This picture is a photomicrograph of the coronal part of a developing tooth prepared to show the organic and cellular constituents which are evident after decalcification and treatment with aniline dyes. In this part of a developing tooth, the relation of the prominent dentinal tubules to the surrounding calcified matrix is well shown. Not shown, however, is the mineralized component and several other organic constituents.

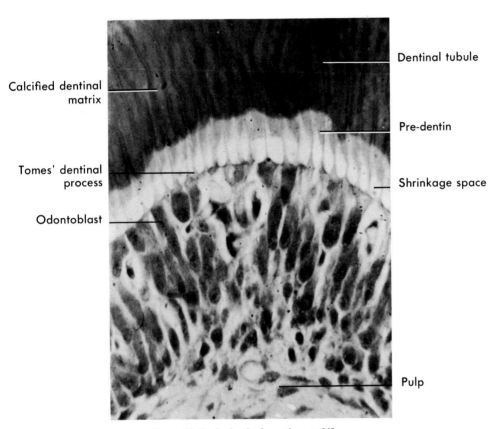

Dentinal tubule

Calcified dentinal matrix

Pre-dentin

Tomes' dentinal process

Shrinkage space

Odontoblast

Pulp

Figure 22. Early dentin formation. ×640.

41

Figure 23. In some of our previous remarks Korff's fibers were mentioned in connection with the formation of dentin. This photomicrograph of a strip of dentin from a nearly completely developed tooth illustrates the manner and degree to which these fibers contribute to the structure of the dental matrix. In the mature tooth these fibers are collagenous. On the periphery of the root they are relatively coarse, whereas in the remainder of the matrix they are more slender in diameter. They occupy a position throughout the entire extent of the dentinal matrix except for the dentinal tubule, the space which is occupied by Tomes' dentinal process. These fibers are the chief structural protein component of dentin exclusive of the dentinal process.

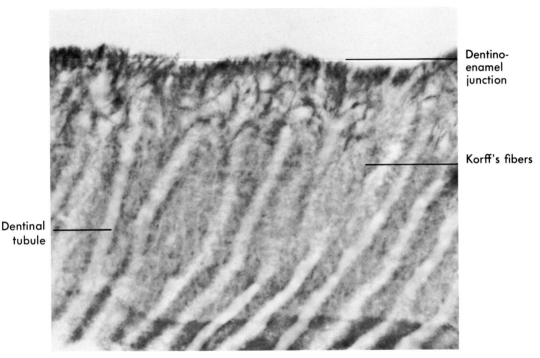

Dentino-
enamel
junction

Korff's fibers

Dentinal
tubule

Figure 23. Distribution of Korff's fibers in dentin. × 1000.

Figure 24. An electron micrograph showing regions of two mature odonto-blasts. In contrast to the young nonsecreting cell, the nucleus, *n*, is located in the distal portion indicating a reversal in polarity: mitochondria, *m*, are prominent as are lipid droplets, *L*. The Golgi apparatus, *G*, also is present. Ribosomes, *r*, are relatively few in number.

44

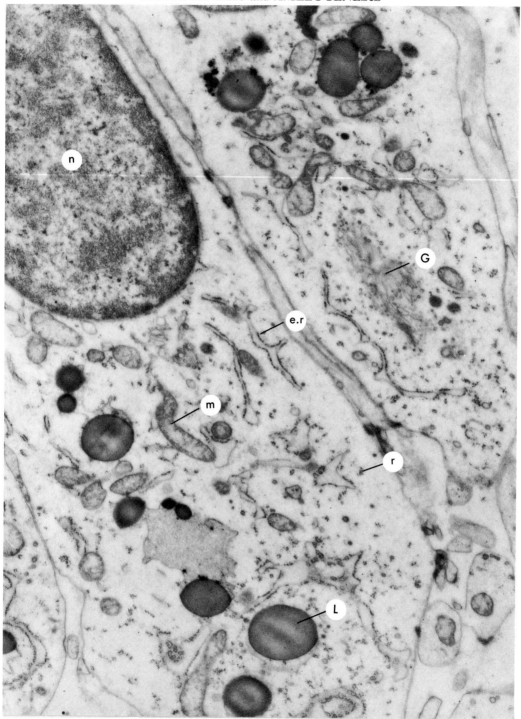

Figure 24. An electron micrograph illustrating mature odontoblast. ×13,000.

3 DENTIN

Figure 25. The ground section of dentin shown here represents a strip of this tissue taken from the region of the dentino-enamel junction. This figure illustrates the manner in which the dentinal tubules tend to branch and divide. Less well shown are the fine subdivisions of the tubules known as tubiculi.

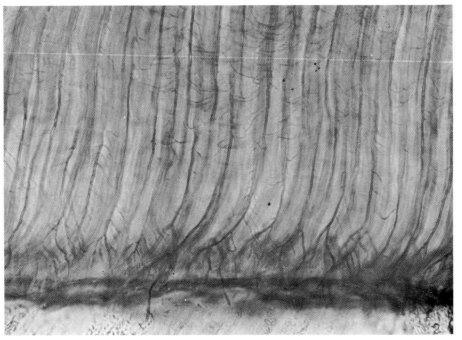

Figure 25. Ground section of dentin (longitudinal). ×640.

Figure 26. The photomicrograph shows a small strip of a ground section of dentin of the root region. This figure also illustrates the branching of the tubules and the delicate tubiculi.

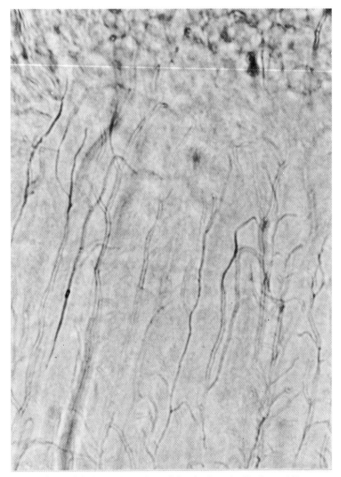

Figure 26. Ground section of dentin (longitudinal). ×640.

Figure 27. A decalcified section 2μ thick of a small area of dentin stained with toluidine blue show the longitudinal arrangement of the dentinal tubules and the surrounding dental matrix. Note also that the tubules are invested by a dark staining outer structure.

Figure 28. The photomicrograph represents a decalcified section of an area of dentin taken from the root of the tooth. This preparation was stained with silver nitrate and shows the profusion of tubiculi which are subdivisions of the dentinal tubules. This morphologic arrangement permits the passage of metabolites to all parts of the dental matrix.

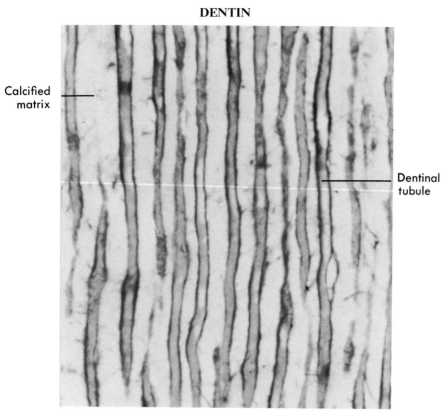

Calcified
matrix

Dentinal
tubule

Figure 27. Decalcified section of dentin. × 1600.

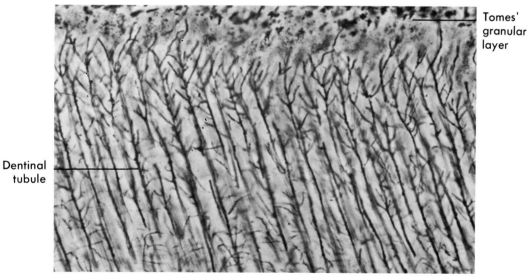

Tomes'
granular
layer

Dentinal
tubule

Figure 28. Decalcified section of dentin (rhesus) showing tubiculi. × 400.

51

Figure 29. This photomicrograph shows a strip of decalcified dentin cut at a thickness of 2μ. It shows the manner in which the dentinal tubules are arranged in the matrix and also the extensive branching of the tubules, the dental tubiculi.

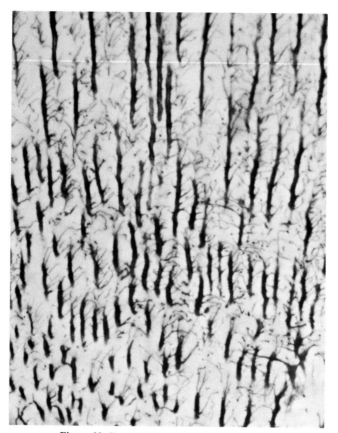

Figure 29. Decalcified section of dentin. ×640.

Figure 30. The electron micrograph represents part of a mature odontoblast and part of the pre-dentin, *p.d.* The appearance of this cell is different in many respects from those shown earlier as follows: The nucleus, *n,* has shifted to a distal position; the endoplasmic reticulum is greatly reduced, as are the ribosomes. Several lipid droplets, *L,* are present. In the state of development of these cells prior to mineralization the organelles are chiefly supranuclear in position. In the cell illustrated, a mature quiescent cell, the nucleus is in the distal third and the organelles are below the nucleus.

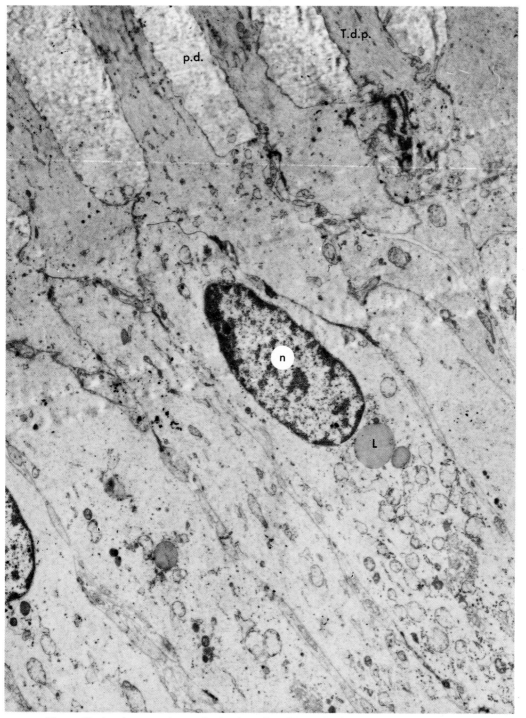

Figure 30. An electron micrograph showing odontoblasts, dentinal tubules and pre-dentin in mature tooth. ×5000.

DENTIN

Figure 31. This electron micrograph illustrates the appearance of a small area of mature calcified dentin. The dark areas represent the calcified dental matrix, *c.d.m.*, which consists of closely packed hydroxyapatite crystals.

Korff's fibers are not shown since this dentin was not decalcified. Between the two dark strips of mineralized dentin one may observe light appearing structure, Tomes' dentinal process, *T.d.p.* These structures are in intimate association with the mineralized matrix and exhibit a delicate fibrillar appearance.

Figure 32. The ground section of dentin shows the dentinal tubules in transverse section. Examination of this micrograph shows the dentinal tubules fairly close to one another, which is typical of dentin in this region of the root. The area not occupied by the tubules is the dental matrix. The elevated appearance of the dentinal tubules is an optical artifact.

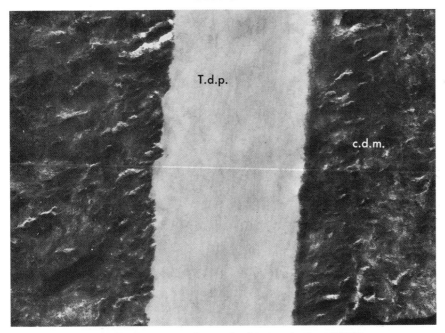

Figure 31. An electron micrograph of mature dentin. × 15,000.

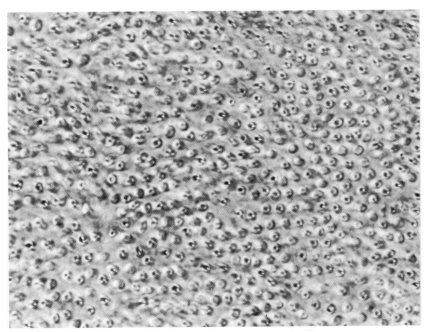

Figure 32. Ground transverse section of dentin. × 640.

57

Figure 33. This decalcified section of dentin shows the dentinal tubules in transverse section. This micrograph was prepared from a 2μ section and stained with toluidine blue. A noteworthy characteristic of the dentinal tubules shown is the dark staining peripheral band immediately surrounding the tubule. This structure is known as Newman's sheath. There is some controversy regarding this structure. Although well shown by the optical light microscope, it is not evident in electron micrographs.

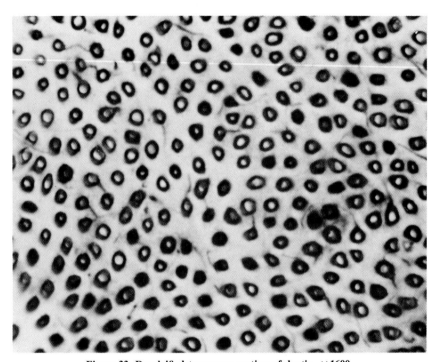

Figure 33. Decalcified transverse section of dentin. × 1600.

Figure 34. An electron micrograph of a small area of undecalcified dentin showing the structure of the dentinal tubules, *d.t.,* and their relation to the calcified matrix, *c.m.* Note that the dentinal tubule is completely filled with the proplasmic fibril which appears relatively homogeneous in this micrograph. The tubule itself is surrounded by a dense membrane-like structure which is in intimate association with the surrounding mineralized matrix. The regions of the matrix show the presence of crystals. At this magnification, however, they are not clearly defined. This type of preparation does not reveal the presence of Korff's fibers, which are nevertheless present in mineralized dentin.

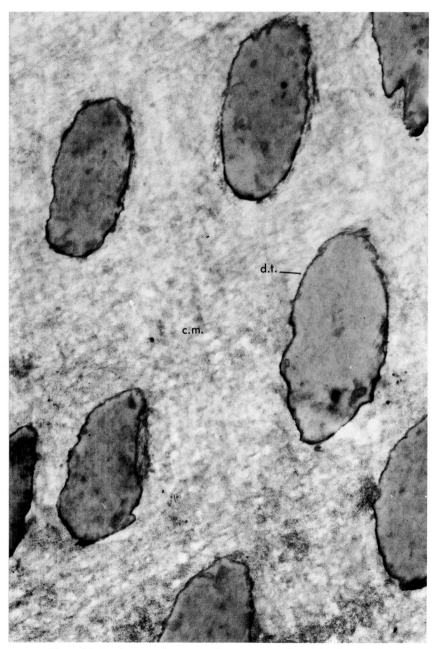

Figure 34. An electron micrograph of transverse section of dentin. ×8500.

DENTIN

Figure 35.   In certain areas of dentin the region surrounding the dentinal tubules mineralizes to a greater extent than the surrounding matrix. When using the electron microscope one observes a darkened area adjacent to the wall of the dentinal tubule, which is indicative of a more highly mineralized area. This part of the matrix is referred to as peritubular dentin. (Courtesy Dr. David Scott.)

Figure 36.   During the developmental period in which the tooth forms, most of the dentin found in the mature tooth is elaborated. It will be recalled, however, that the pulp chamber is relatively large and dentin continues to form for some time after eruption. At some stage after eruption, the character of dentin formed takes on a somewhat different appearance from that more peripherally located. As shown here the circumpulpally located zone known as secondary dentin appears somewhat more irregular and more dense when viewed by transmitted light. This zone of secondary pulpally located dentin is present in all erupted and mature teeth. The reason for the formation of the modified dentin is not well understood.

DENTIN

Dentinal tubule   Matrix   Peritubular dentin

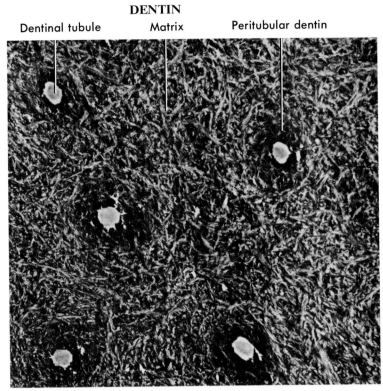

Figure 35. An electron micrograph of undecalcified human dentin. × 4000.

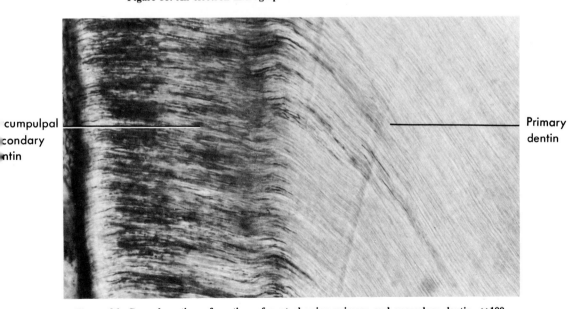

cumpulpal
condary
ntin

Primary
dentin

Figure 36. Ground section of portion of root showing primary and secondary dentin. ×100.

63

INTERGLOBULAR DENTIN

Figure 37, A and B. In many mature teeth examination of certain areas, particularly in the region of the dentino-enamel junction, shows a defect in mineralization. When examined in ground sections, these areas appear as dark crescentic patches which may be few in number or numerous and widely distributed. These areas, known as interglobular dentin, represent parts of the dentin in which mineralization is deficient—areas of hypomineralization. Insofar as it is known, this condition does not affect the well-being of the tooth.

Interglobular
area

Figure 37. Ground sections of dentin showing interglobular areas. *A*, × 400; *B*, × 640. (Bevelander, *Outline of Histology*, courtesy of the C. V. Mosby Co.)

65

GLOBULAR DENTIN

Figure 38. The micrograph represents the appearance of an area of decalcified dentin which is characterized by the presence of globules of dark-staining matrix. This is known as globular dentin and the dark areas are known as calcoglobules. The appearance of the dental matrix shown here is often observed as the first dentin to be formed. It is an example of incompletely mineralized dentin. Dentin having this appearance may also at times be observed in mature teeth.

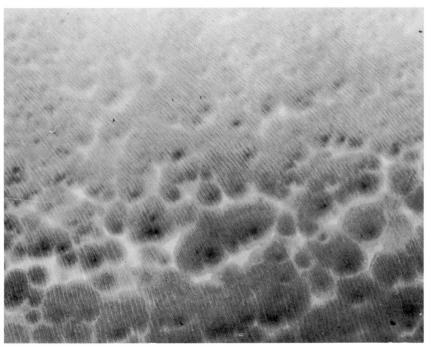

Figure 38. Decalcified section of dentin showing globular pattern of mineralization. ×400.

DEAD TRACTS DUE TO ATTRITION

Figure 39. The photomicrograph illustrates the coronal part of a central tooth which has undergone considerable abrasion of the incisal surface. As a result, the dentinal tubules beneath this area have become devitalized. This in turn gives rise to a wedge-shaped collection of dark tubules known as a dead tract. In conjunction with the loss of vitality of this large number of dentinal tubules, the vital pulp can and does produce a type of secondary (reparative) dentin directly under the devitalized tubules. This is a protective reaction on the part of the pulp in an attempt to seal off this area of the tooth.

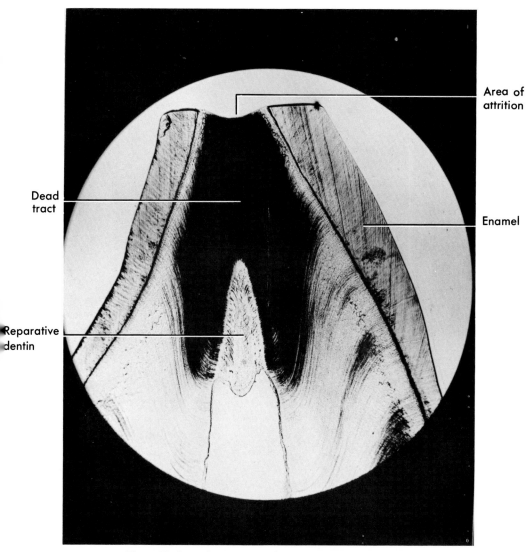

Area of
attrition

Dead
tract

Enamel

Reparative
dentin

Figure 39. Ground section of incisor showing dead tract. ×40.

69

DEAD TRACTS DUE TO CARIES

Figure 40. The photograph represents a ground section of an anterior tooth cut in a mesiodistal plane. Of particular interest is the presence of two dead tracts in the coronal part of the root. These tracts are like those described in the previous account, but differ in that they were formed as a result of carious lesions.

DEAD TRACTS DUE TO CARIES

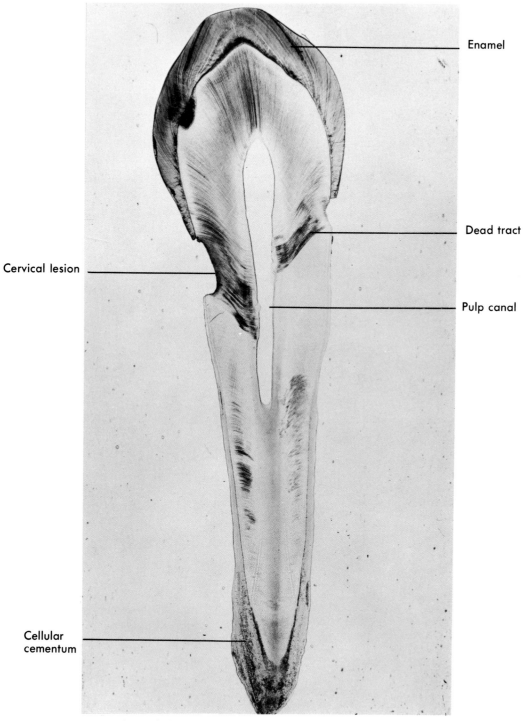

Enamel

Dead tract

Cervical lesion

Pulp canal

Cellular cementum

Figure 40. Ground section of tooth showing dead tracts. ×6.5.

REPARATIVE DENTIN FOLLOWING CARIES

Figure 41. It was previously shown that in a situation in which a dead tract results from incisal abrasion, reparative dentin forms below the region of the tract. This response also occurs when dead tracts occur as a result of the trauma set up when caries occurs. As illustrated here, the vital pulp can and often does attempt to protect itself from the invasion of noxious material by elaborating a mass of reparative dentin, which often serves as an effective barrier between the pulp and the oral environment.

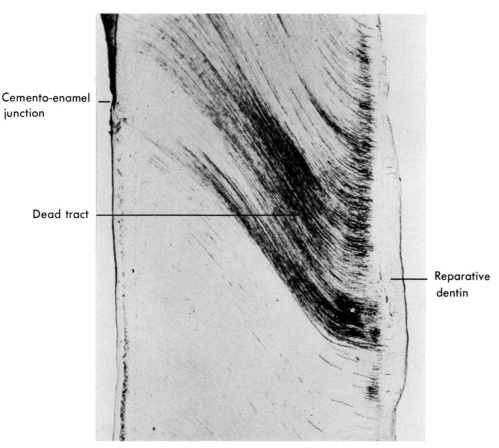

Cemento-enamel
junction

Dead tract

Reparative
dentin

Figure 41. Detail of dead tract and reparative dentin (ground section). ×40.

73

REPARATIVE DENTIN FOLLOWING CAVITY PREPARATION

Figure 42. In many situations involving cavity preparation it is desirable and beneficial to have more dentin available between the base of the cavity preparation and the pulp than the amount retained following operative procedures. In most situations this may be effected by resorting to the use of temporary filling and allowing the tooth itself to effect a thickening of dentin in the area which has been traumatized. This illustration is an example of the formation of reparative dentin in the pulp directly under the dentinal tubules which were cut in connection with cavity preparation.

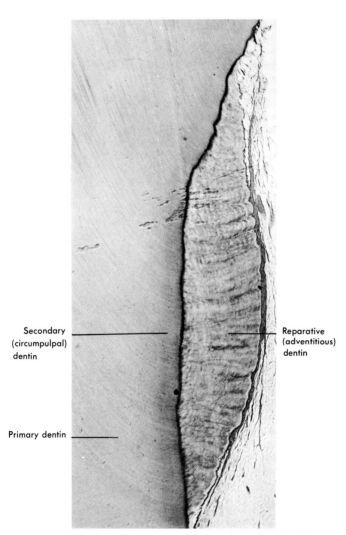

Secondary (circumpulpal) dentin

Reparative (adventitious) dentin

Primary dentin

Figure 42. Detail of reparative dentin (decalcified section). ×50.

TOMES' GRANULAR LAYER

Figure 43. The ground section of a strip of root dentin shows that the peripheral portion of the dentin exhibits an appearance differing from that of the remainder of the dentin. It has a coarse granular appearance in contrast to the well defined tubular appearance of the adjacent dentin. This zone is known as Tomes' granular layer. It probably takes on this appearance because Korff's fibers in this part of the dentin are numerous and dense.

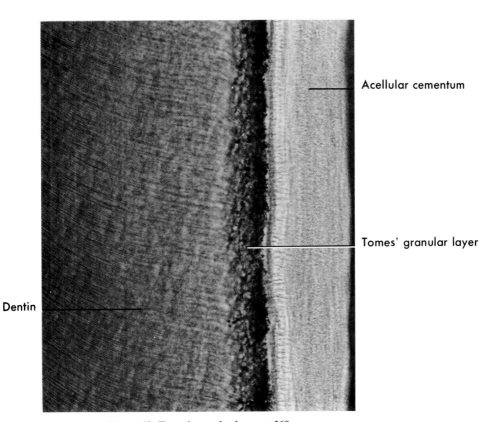

Acellular cementum

Tomes' granular layer

Dentin

Figure 43. Tomes' granular layer. × 160.

DENTINOGENESIS IMPERFECTA

Figure 44. As the name implies this dentin is imperfectly formed, that is to say, during the period of histo-differentiation and mineralization a modification of normal developmental events occurs. The illustration shows that the dentinal tubules are irregularly arranged. The teeth of children exhibiting this condition are soft and are often lost early in life.

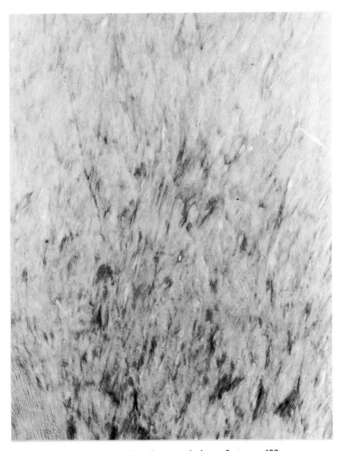

Figure 44. Dentinogenesis imperfecta. ×400.

EFFECT OF VITAMIN D DEFICIENCY

Figure 45. It is well known that disturbances of diverse metabolic processes which occur during the time teeth are being formed may result in the development of teeth exhibiting malformations of several kinds. This illustration shows the interruption in normal mineralization of dentin, which was brought about by placing rats on a diet deficient in vitamin D. It is well known that adequate amounts of this vitamin are necessary for normal mineralization. Examination of this micrograph shows light and dark bands in the dentin formed during the experimental period, indicative of areas deficient in minerals.

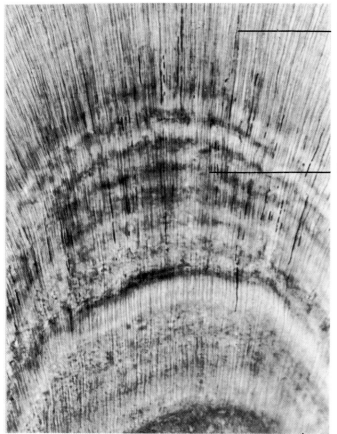

Normal dentin

Dentin in vitamin D deficiency

Figure 45. Effect of vitamin D deficiency. ×400.

4 ENAMEL

Figure 46. This photomicrograph of a ground section of an anterior tooth at low magnification is included here for purposes of orientation. The enamel on the labial aspect is somewhat thicker than on the lingual. Irregularities are due to processing. Note that the dentinal tubules vary in direction in different parts of the tooth and also that the root dentin is transparent. Also shown is the size and extent of the root canal, as well as the cemento-enamel junction which is an important clinical landmark. A thin layer of cementum is shown on the periphery of the root.

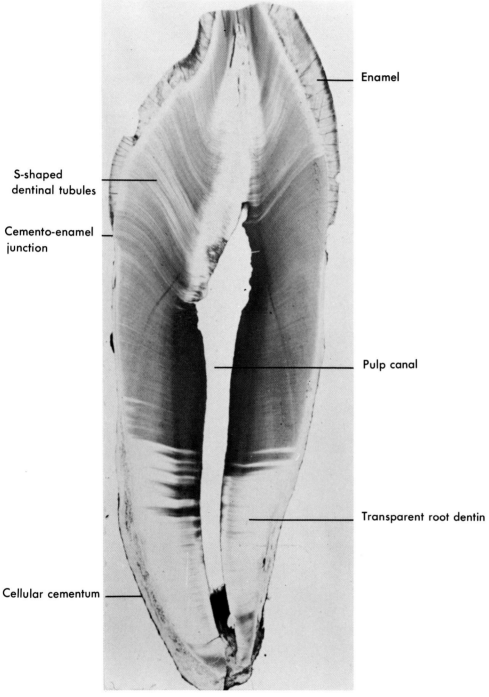

S-shaped
dentinal tubules

Cemento-enamel
junction

Enamel

Pulp canal

Transparent root dentin

Cellular cementum

Figure 46. Ground section of anterior tooth. ×8.

Figure 47. A strip of young enamel is shown in relation to the ameloblasts. Note the elongated nature of these cells. Also shown are the basal nuclei, indicating a reversal of polarity from that observed in pre-functional cells. Tomes' enamel processes are the continuations of the ameloblasts. One may also observe that the enamel rods are arranged in a somewhat wavy fashion and are separated by a space known as the interprismatic space or region. This enamel was incompletely calcified.

Tomes' enamel
process

Stratum
intermedium

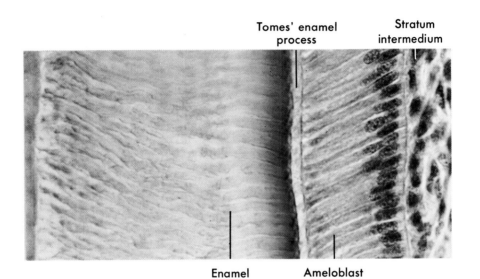

Enamel
rod

Ameloblast

Figure 47. Partially developed enamel. × 640.

ENAMEL

Figure 48. The structural unit of enamel is the enamel rod or prism. In longitudinal section, the rods are arranged in straight rows. They are bounded by a dense membrane, the rod sheath, and are interrupted at regular intervals by cross striations. The rods are separated by a space also mineralized, the interprismatic space.

Figure 49. It was pointed out that the arrangement of the enamel rods shown in Figure 48 was essentially an array of straight rods. This is not true for many areas of enamel. A common variation in this arrangement is shown.

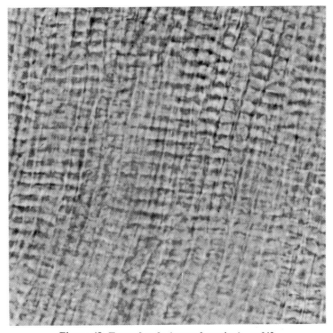

Figure 48. Enamel rods (ground section). ×640.

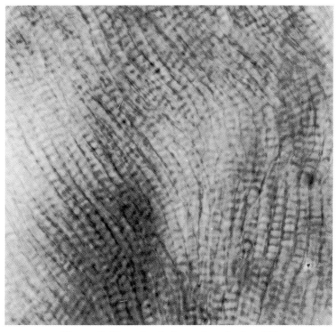

Figure 49. Enamel rods (ground section). ×640.

Figure 50. A much greater variation in the straight arrangement of enamel rods is shown. In this example we observe bundles of enamel rods arranged approximately at right angles to one another.

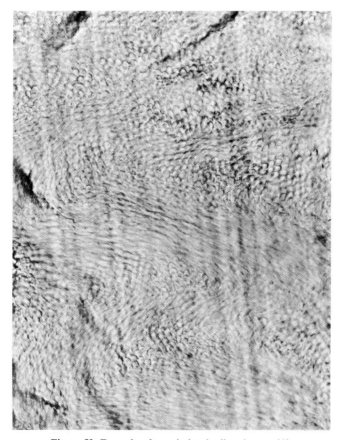

Figure 50. Enamel rods, variation in direction. ×640.

Figure 51. An electron micrograph showing the area of enamel formation. The dark needle-shaped structures represent immature hydroxyapatite crystals. The developing enamel rods, *e.r.,* appear to encroach upon and mineralize Tomes' enamel process, *T.e.p.* In the interprismatic substance, *i.p.s.,* the crystals are aligned at an angle to those in the enamel rods.

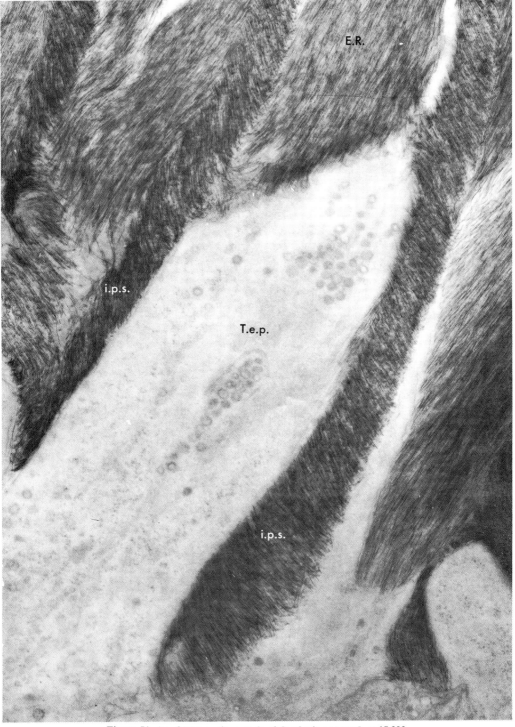

Figure 51. An electron micrograph of developing enamel. ×15,000.

Figure 52. The electron micrograph illustrates a section of immature enamel cut so as to show the arrangement of the rods, *E.R.*, in a longitudinal aspect and also the adjacent mineralized area, the interprismatic substance, *i.p.s.* The dark needle-shaped structures are hydroxyapatite crystals. These crystals are embedded in an organic substrate, eukeratin.

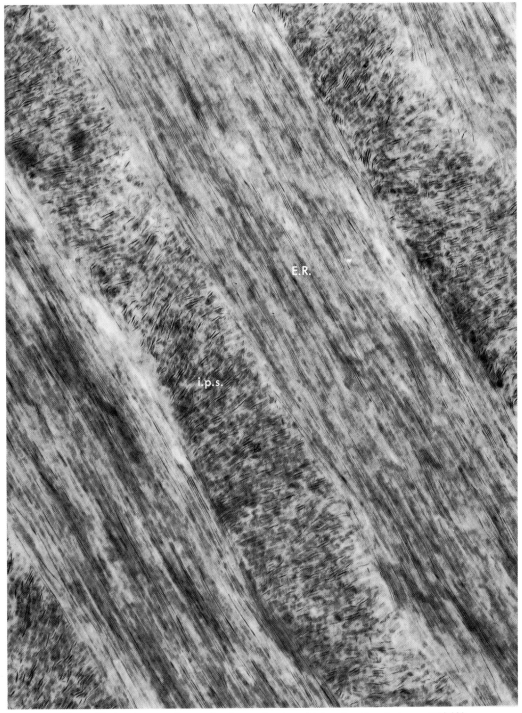

Figure 52. An electron micrograph of enamel rods and interprismatic substance. ×30,000.

Figure 53. When enamel rods are observed following sectioning to show the transverse aspect of the rods, they appear as irregular circular structures. Each rod is enclosed by a membrane, the enamel rod sheath.

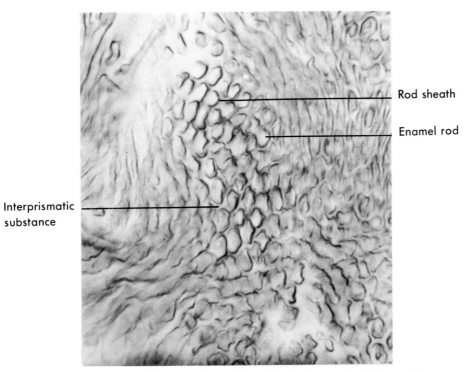

Rod sheath

Enamel rod

Interprismatic
substance

Figure 53. Transverse ground section of enamel. ×640. (Bevelander, G.: *Outline of Histology.*
6th Ed. St. Louis, C. V. Mosby Co.)

Figure 54. This electron micrograph represents an area of immature enamel cut transversely in reference to the direction of the enamel rods. It would appear from an examination of this micrograph that the enamel rods, *E.R.,* are more densely packed with crystals than the surrounding interprismatic substance, *i.p.s.*

Figure 54. An electron micrograph of transverse section of enamel. ×27,000.

ENAMEL SPINDLES

Figure 55. During the early formation of dentin and enamel, the dentinal tubules occasionally protrude into the area destined to be occupied by enamel. These tubules give rise to club-shaped structures which appear dark in ground sections. They represent areas of hypomineralization and are known as enamel spindles.

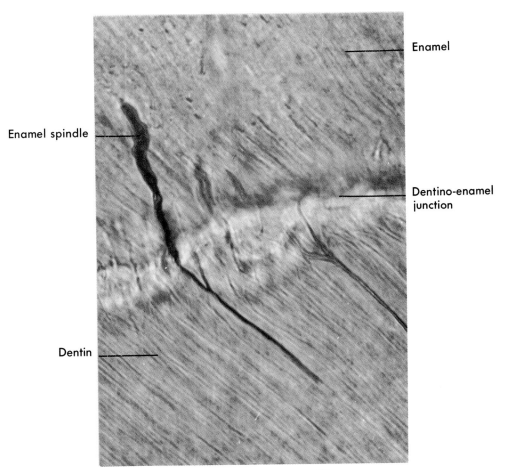

Enamel

Enamel spindle

Dentino-enamel
junction

Dentin

Figure 55. Enamel spindle. ×640.

ENAMEL TUFTS

Figure 56. Another group of structures common to enamel are the enamel tufts. They are most readily observed in transverse ground sections of enamel. They consist of ribbon-like sheets of organic material incompletely mineralized. They originate at the dentino-enamel junction and extend less than one-third the width of the enamel.

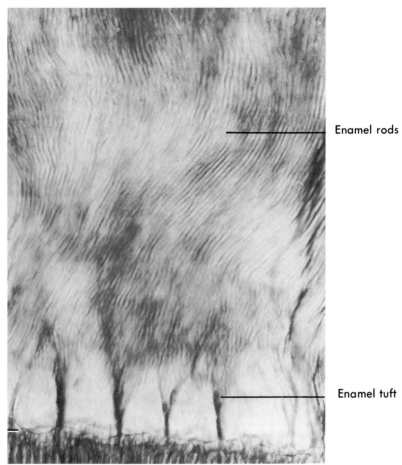

Enamel rods

Enamel tuft

Dentino-enamel
junction

Figure 56. Enamel tufts. ×420. (Bevelander, G.: *Outline of Histology*. 6th Ed. St. Louis, C. V. Mosby Co.)

ENAMEL LAMELLA

Figure 57. The lamellae are similar to the tufts except for the fact that they extend throughout the entire width of the enamel and do not appear tuft- or fan-like. Since these structures extend to the enamel surface and are hypomineralized sheets of organic material, they may afford entry into the enamel by bacteria.

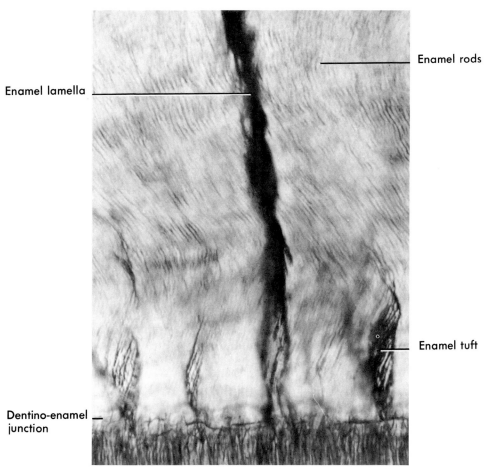

Enamel rods

Enamel lamella

Enamel tuft

Dentino-enamel
junction

Figure 57. Enamel lamella. ×640. (Bevelander, G.: *Outline of Histology*. 6th Ed. St. Louis, C. V. Mosby Co.)

103

INCREMENTAL LINES (OF RETZIUS)

Figure 58. Enamel is elaborated in a rhythmic incremental fashion and during this process there are either interruptions or a change in the rate of deposition, which modifies the structure and appearance of enamel in such a way that ground sections of enamel appear striated. These striations or stripes are known as the incremental lines or striae of Retzius.

Figure 59.   When a transverse section of the crown of the tooth is prepared and examined with the microscope, the striae of Retzius appear as a series of dark concentric rings.

Figure 58. Striae of Retzius. × 45.

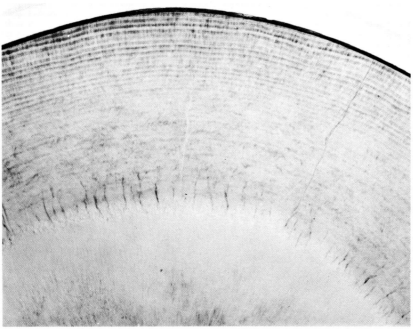

Figure 59. Striae of Retzius in transverse section. × 40.

Figure 60. The photomicrograph shows an area of enamel in the cervical part of the tooth which was sectioned in a longitudinal plane. Examination of a ground section of the crown of a tooth in which these lines are prominent reveal the time sequence of enamel formation.

Figure 61. This strip of enamel shows lines of Retzius at higher magnification. One may observe that dark portions giving rise to the lines vary in width, and the distance between the lines varies considerably, which suggests that the cause of these modifications were diverse in time and intensity.

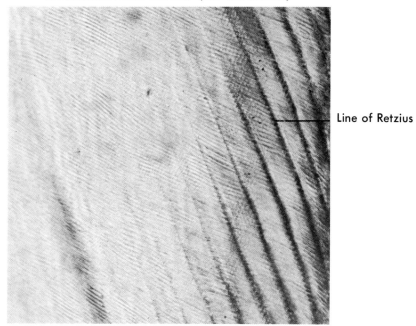

Line of Retzius

Figure 60. Striae of Retzius in longitudinal section. × 40.

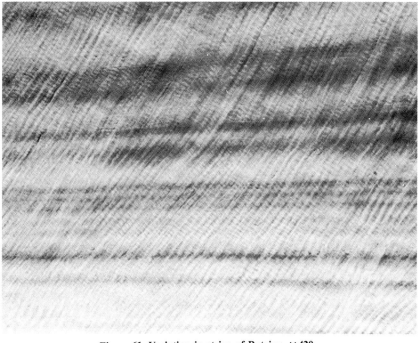

Figure 61. Variation in striae of Retzius. × 420.

107

HUNTER-SCHREGER BANDS

Figure 62. In describing the direction of enamel rods it was previously shown that they were arranged in various directions. This is well exemplified in this photomicrograph taken by means of reflected light. By the use of this device, one may often see that the enamel appears as alternating dark and light bands. These are the Hunter-Schreger bands and this optical effect is due to the fact that the enamel rods in the adjacent areas are arranged approximately at right angles to one another.

Figure 62. Hunter-Schreger bands. ×40.

PITS AND FISSURES

Figure 63. In the multicuspid tooth the area at the junction of the cusps is the last part of the enamel to be elaborated and presents some interesting morphologic features which are of clinical interest. These areas at the site of the union of adjacent cusps are arranged in such a manner that a pit or fissure is present and partially separates the adjoining cusps. These indentations often extend nearly to the surface of the underlying dentin.

The anatomic arrangement affords a space in which food and other detritus easily accumulates and is retained. Under these conditions an environment conducive to bacterial growth and subsequent destruction of the enamel frequently occurs. Two other important facts regarding this area are: (1) the enamel is much thinner than in other parts of the crown; and (2) the direction of the enamel rods are arranged at an oblique angle in reference to the surface of the enamel pit.

Figure 63. Crown of tooth showing pit at junction of cusps. ×15.

CARIES

Figure 64. The photograph of the coronal part of the tooth illustrates a change in the region of the pit mentioned previously. In this specimen the enamel in region of the pit appears dark, indicative of early caries formation. Also shown is a cone of dentin immediately subjacent to the dark enamel which appears much lighter than the surrounding dentin. The light cone of dentin is also undergoing retrogressive changes as a result of the carious lesion with which it is in contact.

112

Enamel caries

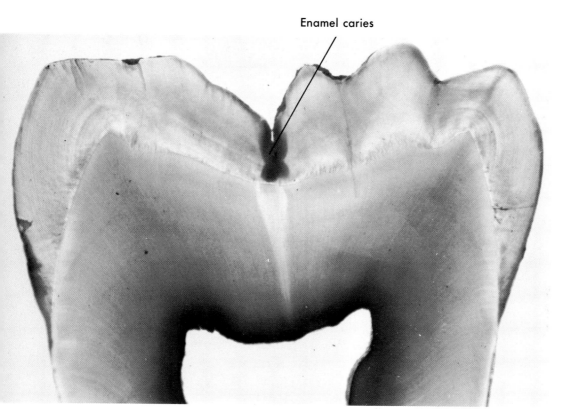

Figure 64. Caries formation in region of pit. ×15.

DIRECTION OF ENAMEL RODS IN CERVICAL AREA

Figure 65 A, B, and C.   The general description in reference to the direction of the enamel rods is usually to the effect that they are arranged at right angles to the dentino-enamel junction. This is probably true for most of the enamel. Exceptions to this arrangement are in the cervical and intercuspal areas, which correspond to cervical areas in structure and time of deposition. Some of the most common arrangements of enamel rods in the cervical region are illustrated: *A,* the rods are nearly straight and at right angles to the junction; *B,* the rods in the region of the cemento-enamel junction are irregularly arranged; and *C,* the rods are at such an angle that they are directed toward the apical part of the tooth.

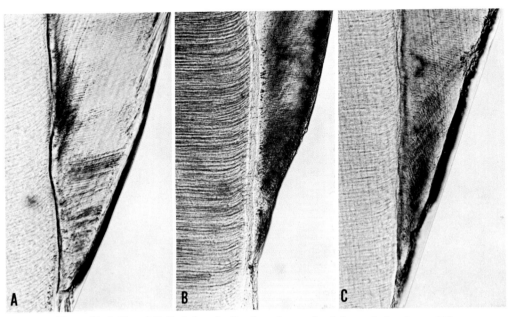

Figure 65. A, B, and C. Variations in direction of enamel rods in cervical region. × 160.

HYPOPLASTIC ENAMEL

Figure 66. It was previously pointed out that when teeth develop during a period of adverse metabolic or other important environmental conditions, they may be adversely affected. A section of a tooth is shown exhibiting a malformation of the crown (enamel) known as enamel hypoplasia, which usually implies a reduction in the normal amount of enamel produced.

Figure 67. At somewhat higher magnification one may observe as shown in Figure 66 some aspects of the hypoplastic tooth in greater detail. The enamel is deficient in amount and also in structure. In regard to this latter feature unusual pigmentation and irregular arrangement of the enamel rods is apparent. The subjacent dentin in the region of the dentino-enamel junction consists of a wide band of interglobular dentin indicative of a rather severe disturbance in mineralization.

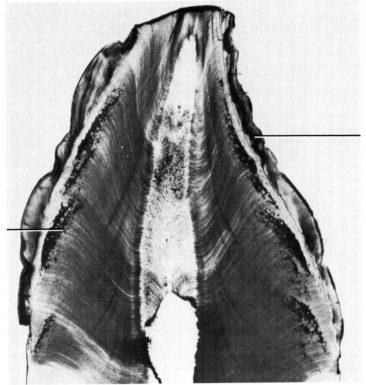

Hypoplastic enamel

Interglobular dentin

Figure 66. Coronal part of tooth exhibiting enamel hypoplasia. × 17.5.

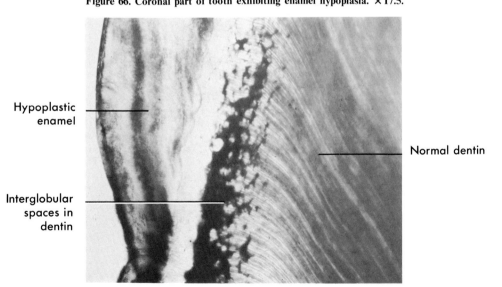

Hypoplastic enamel

Normal dentin

Interglobular spaces in dentin

Figure 67. Detail of hypoplastic enamel. × 60. (Bevelander, G.: *Outline of Histology*. 6th Ed. St. Louis, C. V. Mosby Co.)

5 PULP

TOPOGRAPHY

Figure 68. This photograph illustrates the appearance of the pulp in a newly erupted tooth. Of particular significance is the fact that the pulp horn is extensive and the walls of the tooth in the region of the apex are thin and fragile. This root is incompletely formed and the apical foramen is wide.

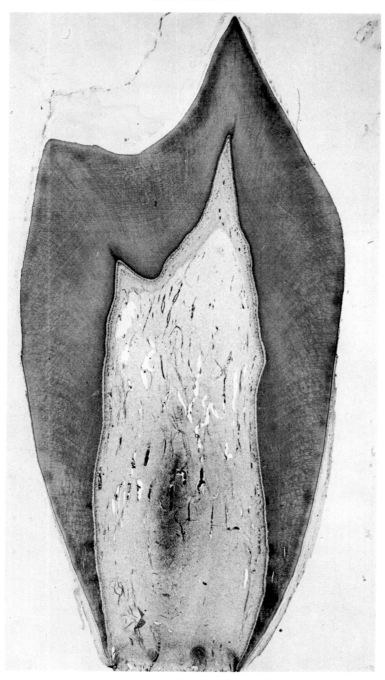

Figure 68. Decalcified section of newly erupted tooth. × 10.

Figure 69. In contrast to the topography of the pulp of a young or newly erupted tooth shown in Figure 68, the section of the mature tooth shown here differs in the following important aspects. The pulp horns are greatly reduced in size. This situation is due to the presence of a greater amount of coronal dentin.

The root canals are also considerably reduced in size and the apical foramina as well. The root of this tooth has completely formed, and relatively little if any change in structure occurs in this state.

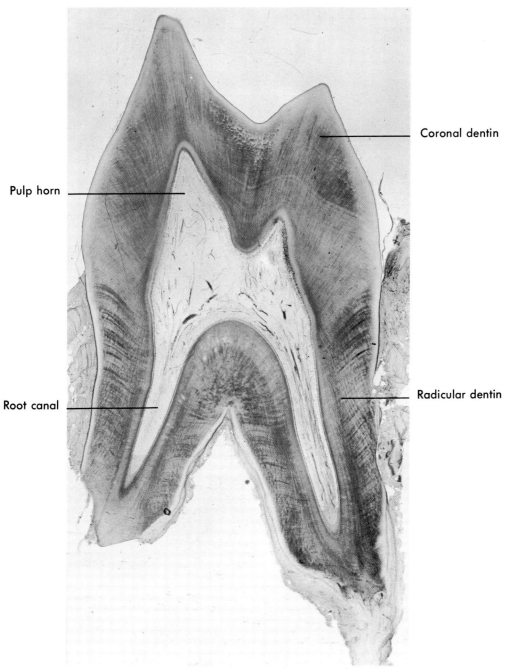

Coronal dentin

Pulp horn

Root canal

Radicular dentin

Figure 69. Decalcified section of mature tooth. ×10.

121

THE APICAL FORAMEN

Figure 70. The apical part of a central tooth and surrounding structures is illustrated. One may observe that the root canal continues to the apical foramen and makes its exit directly in the center of the root. Shown in the root canal is a heavy nerve trunk which almost completely fills this space.

Figure 71. The condition shown in Figure 70 is subject to considerable variation in the place of exit of the pulp to the surrounding regions. There are two conditions in which variations occur. The first is one in which a curvature of the root exists (shown here). The second variation is the occurrence of one or more accessory root canals which, as the name implies, means that additional root canals occur at various levels of the root.

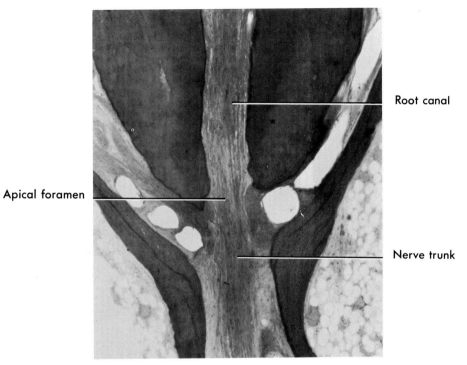

Root canal

Apical foramen

Nerve trunk

Figure 70. Relation of apical foramen to root canal. ×40.

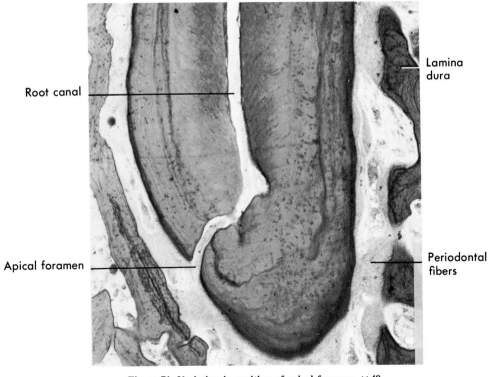

Lamina dura

Root canal

Apical foramen

Periodontal fibers

Figure 71. Variation in position of apical foramen. ×40.

PULP

VASCULARIZATION

Figure 72. This photograph illustrates several features common to the young or newly erupted tooth previously described. It also shows the topographical distribution of the blood vessels that supply the pulp. The vascular elements consist of arterial and venous vessels and probably a lymphatic constituent also. In the young tooth the number and size of the vessels is extensive.

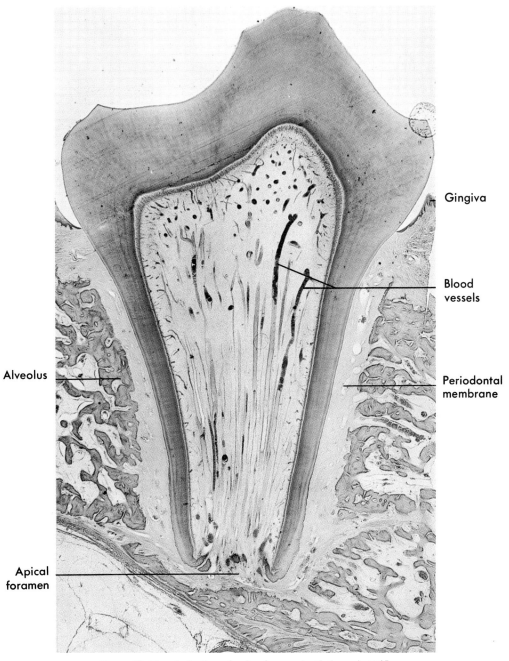

Gingiva

Blood
vessels

Alveolus

Periodontal
membrane

Apical
foramen

Figure 72. Vascularization of pulp of young tooth (puppy). ×15.

125

CELLULAR COMPOSITION

Figure 73. The dental pulp is essentially a connective tissue made up of the constituents common to connective tissue in other parts of the organism. In the pulp of the young tooth the characteristic appearance in section is one in which the most prominent cell is the fibroblast. These cells are numerous and metabolically active. There are relatively few fine connective tissue fibers in the fluid ground substance. This condition is one that indicates a high degree of viability.

126

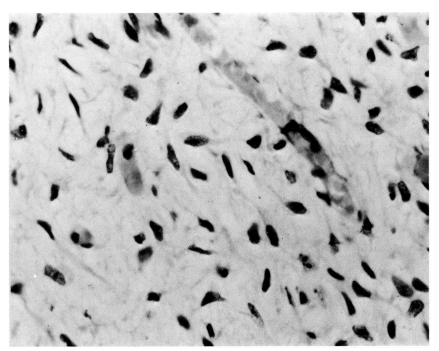

Figure 73. Cellular elements in pulp of newborn. ×640.

Figure 74. The section of a small area of pulp taken from the tooth of a 14-year-old individual, illustrated by this electron micrograph, shows in greater detail the characteristic features of normal pulp. The relation and structure of the fibroblasts, *f,* the relatively few delicate collagenous fibers, *col.,* and the extensive clear spaces occupied by ground substance, *a,* is clearly shown.

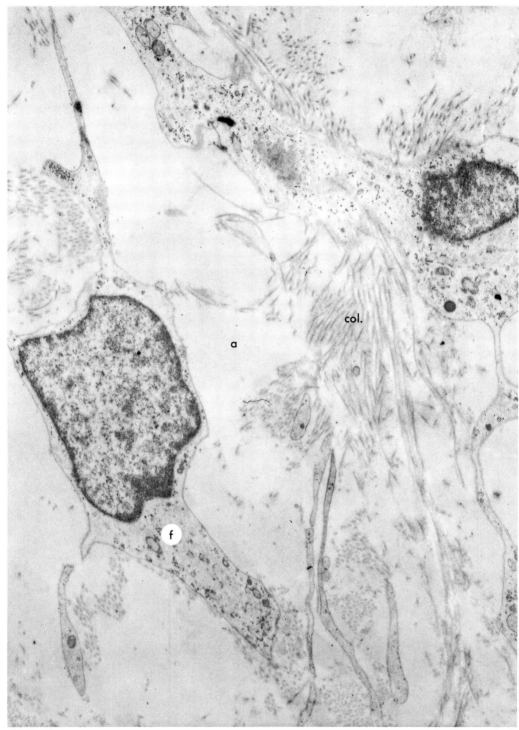

Figure 74. An electron micrograph of pulp of child. ×7800.

Figure 75. This electron micrograph is a section of the pulp from the tooth illustrated in Figure 74. This section, however, was taken from a different level and cut transversely in reference to the long axis of the tooth. Of especial interest are the capillary, *c,* with a red blood cell in the lumen, and the appearance of the fibroblasts, *f,* cut transversely. The fibroblasts are surrounded by scattered bundles of collagen fibers, *col.,* embedded in *a,* the fluid ground substance. This section illustrates the high degree of cellularity of the young pulp.

130

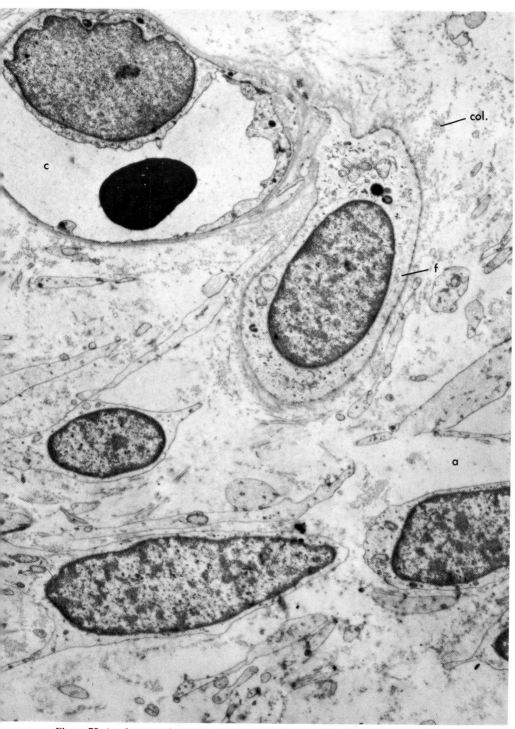

Figure 75. An electron micrograph showing a capillary and fibroblasts in pulp. ×5200.

MATURE PULP

Figure 76. The mature pulp can and does undergo several modifications. These consist first of a reduction in the size of the pulp chamber and a corresponding reduction in tissue, and second in changes in composition of the tissue itself. The composition of normal adult pulp differs from the pulp of the young tooth chiefly by a reduction in cells (fibroblasts) and a relative increase in fibers. Other changes not so obvious by histologic techniques are changes in the chemical composition of the cells, ground substance, and other elements of the pulp.

Figure 77. The vascularity of the pulp is also modified as the tooth ages. Barring infection or injury, however, the pulp is adequately vascularized in the adult. The blood supply to pulp is concerned not only with the pulp cells, but also with the odontoblasts. The vessels nourishing the pulp frequently terminate in the form of loops in the region of the odontoblasts.

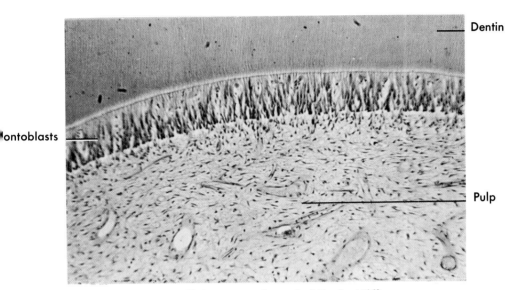

Dentin

ontoblasts

Pulp

Figure 76. Appearance of normal adult pulp. × 160.

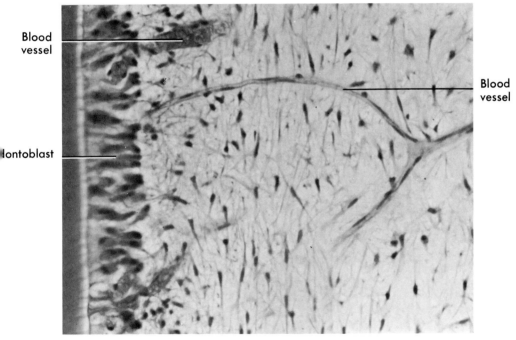

Blood
vessel

Blood
vessel

ontoblast

Figure 77. Blood vessels in pulp. × 400.

133

NERVE SUPPLY

Figure 78. The nerve supply of the pulp enters at the apical foramen and continues throughout the entire pulp by extensive branching, as shown in this decalcified section stained with silver. The nerves are of two kinds: myelinated, which terminate in the region of the dentin, and nonmyelinated, which often accompany blood vessels.

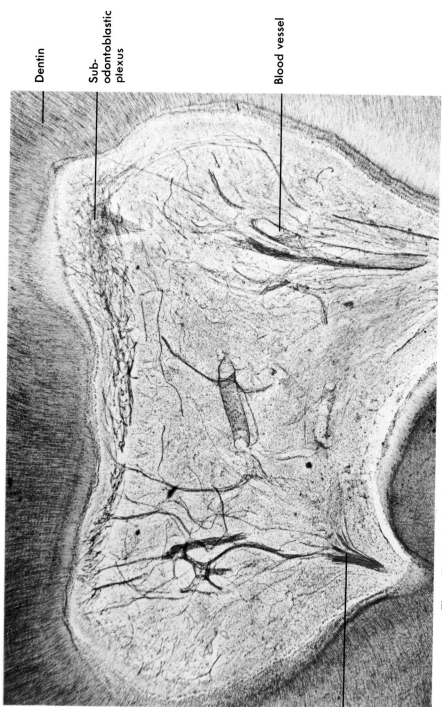

Dentin

Sub-
odontoblastic
plexus

Blood vessel

Nerve trunk

Figure 78. Distribution of nerves in the pulp. ×33. (Specimen courtesy Dr. Sol Bernick.)

135

Figure 79. The nerve trunks that enter the pulp are quite extensive. They are frequently in close association with blood vessels, which they often accompany for considerable distances. Nonmyelinated fibers are extremely difficult to identify in sections of this kind.

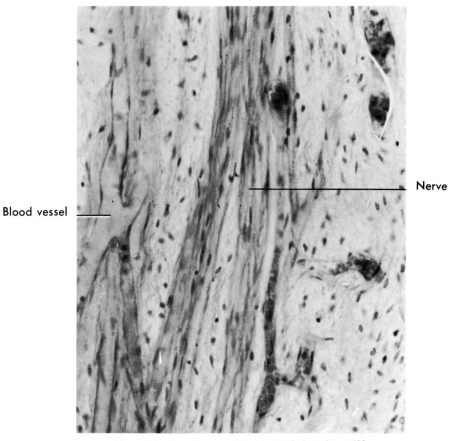

Blood vessel ⎯⎯⎯

Nerve ⎯⎯⎯⎯⎯⎯⎯

Figure 79. Nerve fibers and blood vessels in pulp. ×400.

137

Figure 80. The terminal portions of the myelinated fibers are generally believed to extend as far as the pre-dentin. In this area they may be observed as delicate single beaded structures which sometimes recurve to the pulp after reaching the pre-dentin. They are believed to be responsible for conducting pain impulses.

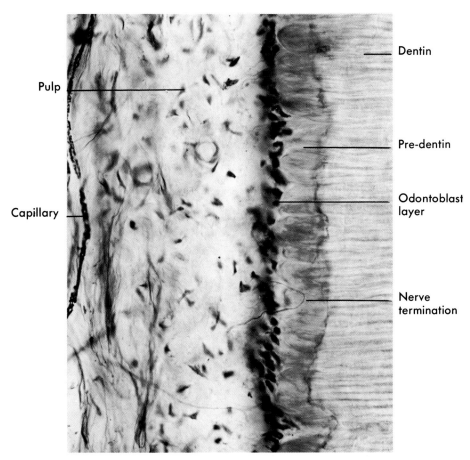

Pulp

Capillary

Dentin

Pre-dentin

Odontoblast layer

Nerve termination

Figure 80. Nerve terminations in pulp. ×400. (Courtesy Dr. Sol Bernick.)

Figure 81. The electron micrograph represents a small portion of the pulp of a 14-year-old child. Pulp is cut transversely in reference to the long axis of the tooth. Of especial interest in this micrograph are the transverse sections of several myelinated nerves, *n,* exhibiting dark coats of myelin and associated with the cell of Schwann. Of equal interest is the presence of the nonmyelinated fibers, *n.m.,* shown with their respective Schwann cells. Also present, as one might expect, are numerous collagen fibers, *col.,* and portions of fibroblasts.

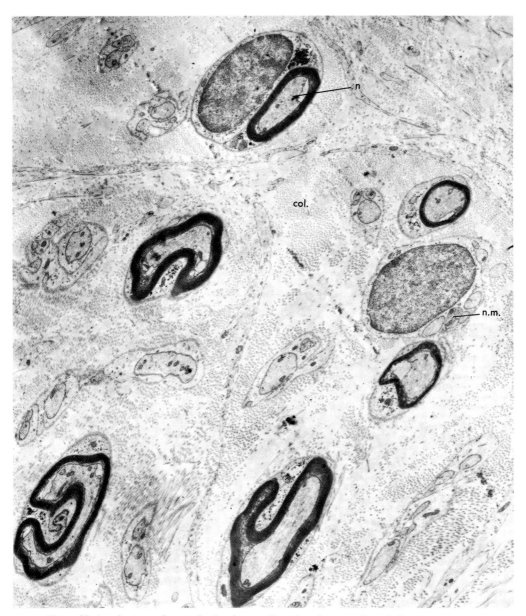

Figure 81. An electron micrograph showing myelinated and nonmyelinated fibers in the pulp. × 5000.

141

RETROGRESSIVE CHANGES

Figure 82. It was previously mentioned that many changes in the cellular composition of the pulp often take place in ageing. One of the most common of these changes is a marked reduction in the number and regressive changes in the fibroblasts (and other cells). In addition there is a corresponding increase in the amount of fibrous tissue and probably in the composition of the ground substance, since this is dependent upon the state of the fibroblasts, the cells which elaborate this substance.

142

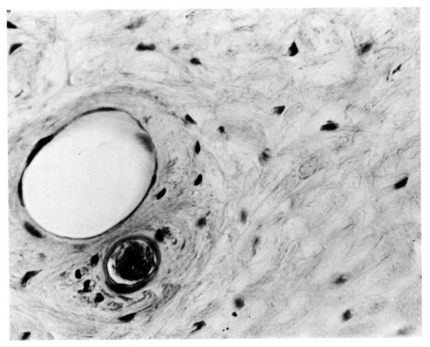

Figure 82. Section of adult pulp showing increase in collagen fibers. ×400.

Figure 83.   Accompanying an increase in fibrous material, another change of a retrogressive nature is observed in the majority of adult teeth. This is brought on by the formation of mineralized areas in the pulp. They are known as pulp stones or denticles and may develop to such a degree as to occupy a considerable part of the pulp in both the pulp horn and the root canal. The presence of pulp stones is not usually accompanied by adverse clinical symptoms. Their presence, however, does indicate that retrogressive changes have taken place.

Figure 84.   The extensive formation of pulp stones may give rise to adverse changes in the structure of the pulp. A portion of pulp is illustrated in which pulp stones were large, numerous, and closely associated. Also shown are pulp stones which are impinging upon a nerve trunk. Other tissue disruption is also evident.

144

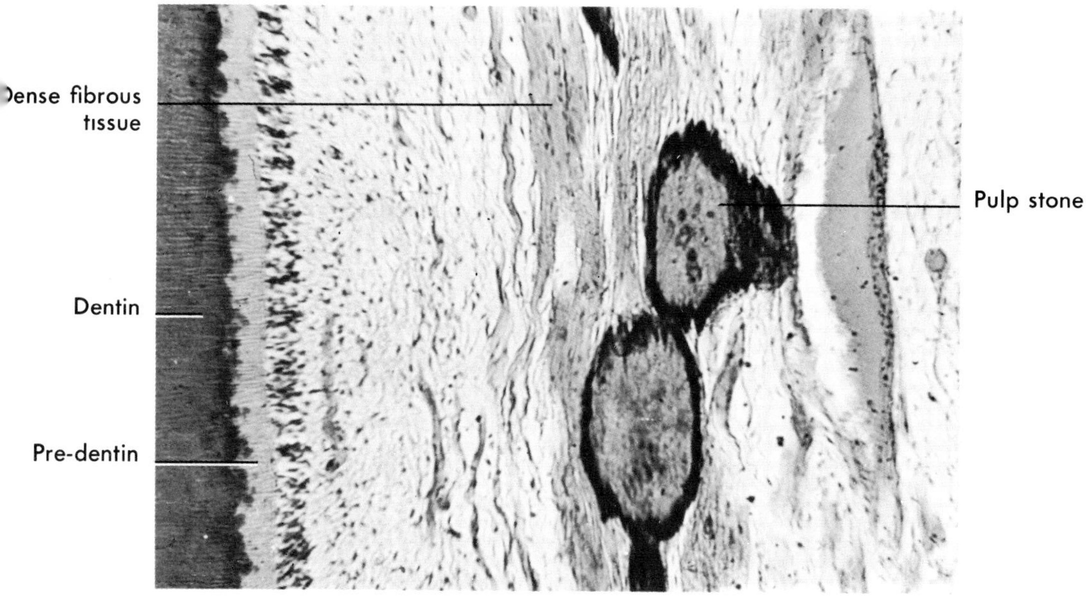

RETROGRESSIVE CHANGES

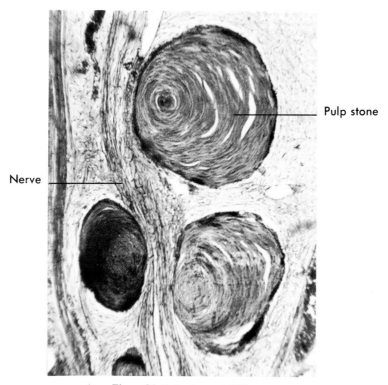

Dense fibrous tissue

Pulp stone

Dentin

Pre-dentin

Figure 83. Pulp stones. × 100.

Pulp stone

Nerve

Figure 84. Pulp stones. × 100.

145

REACTION TO PULP CAPPING

Figure 85. The pulp capping procedure involves the removal of the pulp in the region of the pulp horns, and the subsequent placement of filling material to restore the contour of the pulp and the crown. Under favorable circumstances the pulp responds favorably and elaborates a bridge of secondary dentin. In addition, the apical dentin remains viable and the tooth remains functional. This is another example of the capacity the tooth exhibits to respond with a reparative or protective reaction to adverse conditions.

Figure 86. This photograph illustrates an example of a tooth subjected to the pulp capping procedures. Several years later, the pulp exhibited a severe inflammatory reaction which necessitated the removal of the tooth. This demonstrates again the possible ageing effect upon the viability and resilience of the pulp.

REACTION TO PULP CAPPING

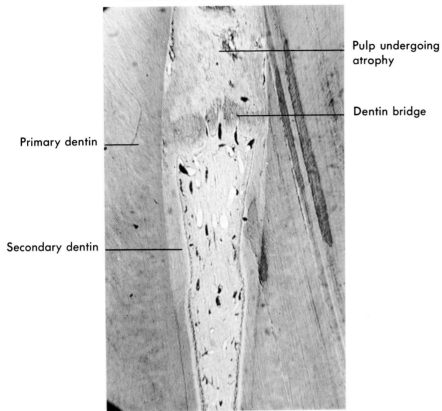

Pulp undergoing atrophy

Dentin bridge

Primary dentin

Secondary dentin

Figure 85. Dentin bridge. × 20.

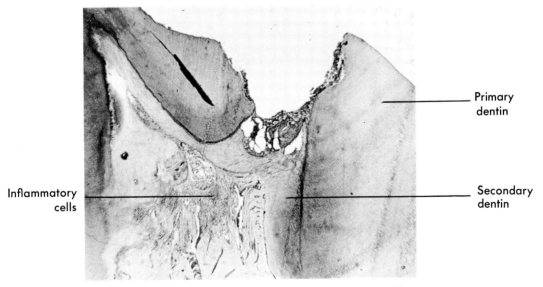

Primary dentin

Inflammatory cells

Secondary dentin

Figure 86. Pulp failure in specimen subjected to pulp capping. × 20.

147

6 CEMENTUM

Figure 87. The cementum is the third mineralized tissue of the tooth. It is formed relatively late in the development of the tooth and the cells responsible for cementum formation are known as cementoblasts. They are derived from mesenchymal cells in the periodontal space and occupy a position adjacent to the root. One variety of cementum appears in ground section as a clear hyaline substance and is known as acellular cementum. It usually occurs in the coronal two-thirds of the root. Another variety, cellular cementum, in which cells (cementocytes) are present, is usually formed later in the life of the tooth and is located as a rule on the apical one-third of the root. The description given above is a general one. The distribution of cementum can and does vary considerably in different teeth. The most important function that cementum serves is to anchor the periodontal fibers in the surface of the root. It may also take part in root repair.

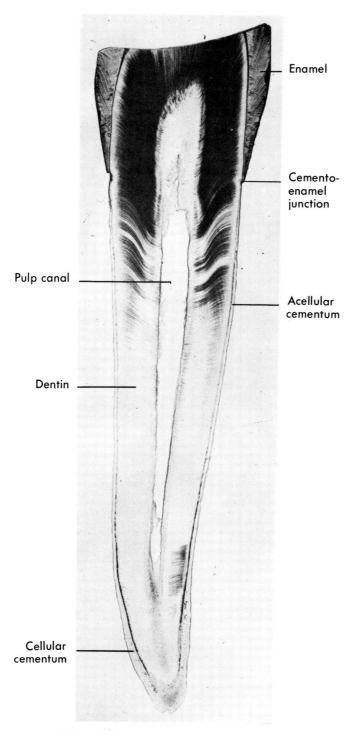

Enamel

Cemento-
enamel
junction

Pulp canal

Acellular
cementum

Dentin

Cellular
cementum

Figure 87. Ground section of lower incisor. ×9.

Figure 88. This photomicrograph illustrates the site occupied by the cemento-blasts in the root of the mature tooth and the relation of the periodontal structures and formed cementum to these cells.

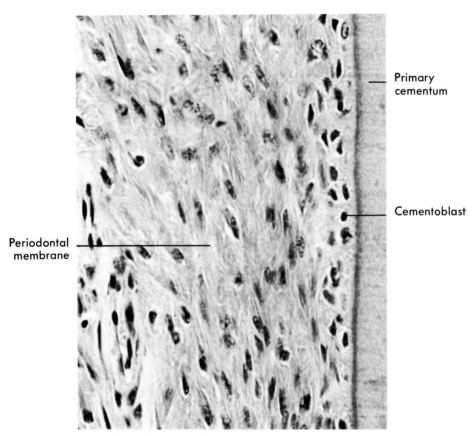

Primary
cementum

Cementoblast

Periodontal
membrane

Figure 88. Cementoblasts in periodontal space. × 160.

151

Figure 89. This photomicrograph represents a transverse section of the root. In addition to the root canal and dentin the surrounding cementum is also shown. Note that the relative width of the cementum varies in different regions of the root.

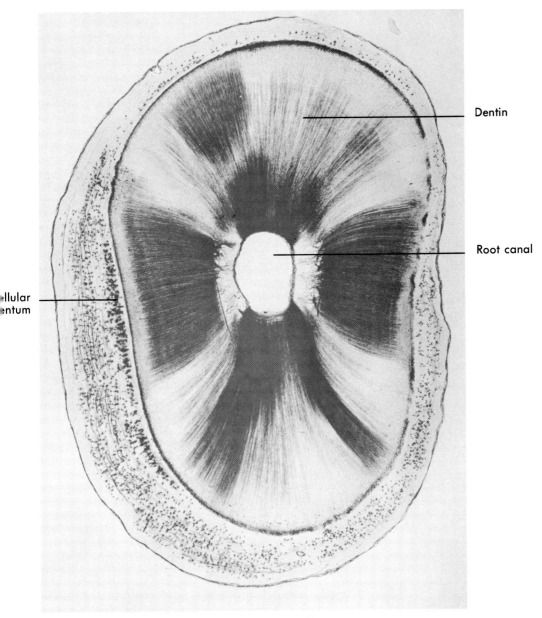

Dentin

Root canal

Cellular
cementum

Figure 89. Transverse section of the root (ground section). ×25.

153

CEMENTUM

Figure 90. The apical part of a root shown here illustrates the amount and kind of cementum that is quite typical for this area.

Figure 91. The photomicrograph illustrates the typical appearance of a ground section of cellular cementum. This tissue showing the spaces occupied by the cementocytes is very similar to bone in appearance and composition.

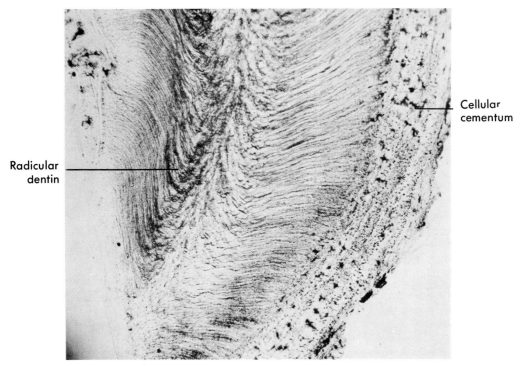

Radicular dentin

Cellular cementum

Figure 90. Cellular cementum. ×12.5.

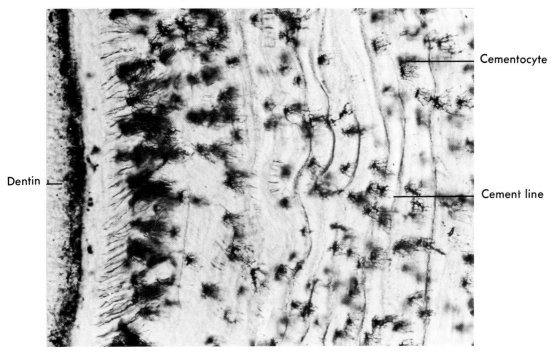

Dentin

Cementocyte

Cement line

Figure 91. Cellular cementum. ×420.

155

Figure 92. This electron micrograph illustrates the detailed structure of a portion of the periodontal space. One may observe bundles of collagen fibers, *col.*, which are inserted into the cementum, *c.c.*, and also the structure of a cementoblast, *n*, located on the periphery of the cementum.

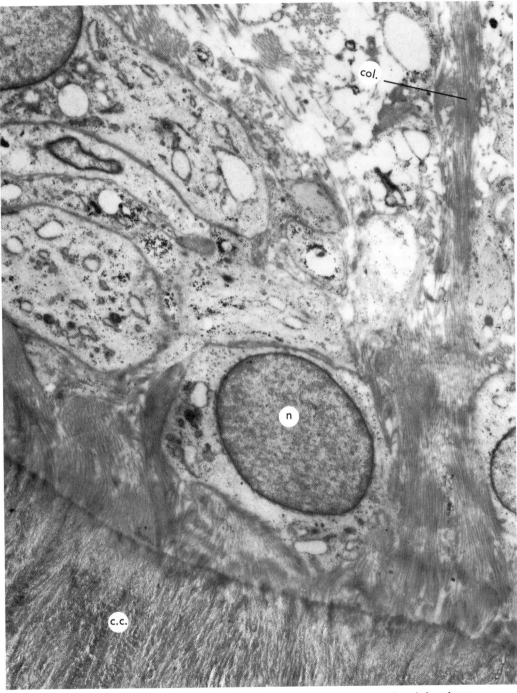

Figure 92. An electron micrograph showing cementum, cementoblasts, and periodontal membrane. ×8000.

157

Figure 93. An electron micrograph of the peripheral part of the cementum which was not demineralized shows the appearance of calcified cementum, *c.c.,* under these conditions. The fibers penetrating the cementum, *col.,* are not as well shown as in Figure 92 owing to the presence of the mineral crystals. The mineral composition of cementum is similar to that of bone.

Figure 93. An electron micrograph illustrating appearance of cementum. × 12,000.

7 THE SUPPORTING APPARATUS

PERIODONTAL MEMBRANE

Figure 94. The periodontal membrane consists of a group of connective tissue fibers which maintain the gingiva in close proximity to the cervical part of the tooth and support the tooth in the socket. The fibers in the root region are arranged in different directions and are inserted in the bony alveolus on one side and the cementum of the tooth on the opposite side. The width of the space occupied by this membrane varies in different teeth and in different parts of the same tooth. It is usually narrowest at a point one-third the distance to the root and varies in dimension from approximately 10 to 25 mm in width. Several of the component parts of the supporting apparatus are shown.

PERIODONTAL MEMBRANE

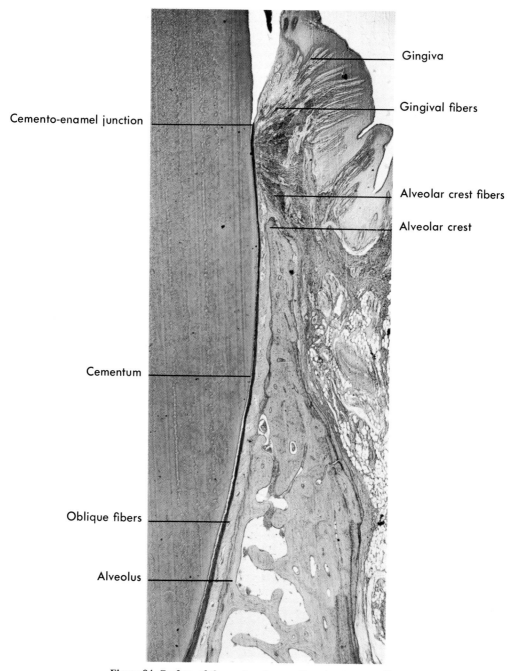

Figure 94. Surface of the root and supporting structures. ×18.

Figure 95. During the development of the tooth the fibers of the dental sac give rise to fibers subsequently recognized as periodontal fibers. Before eruption many of the fibers are arranged parallel to the long axis of the tooth as shown here (silver stain).

Figure 96. The periodontal membrane is made up of several groups of fibers, including the *gingival fibers* which originate at the site of the cemento-enamel junction and fan out to the lamina propria of the gingiva (Fig. 94). Another group of fibers originates at the alveolar crest and extends to the region below the cemento-enamel junction. They are known as the *alveolar crest fibers.*

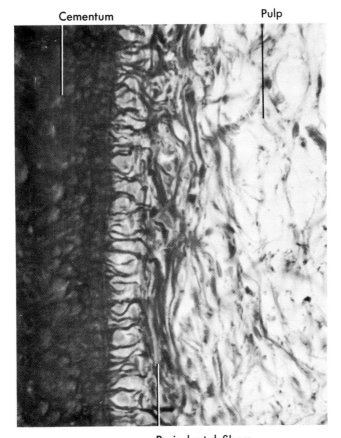

Cementum   Pulp

Periodontal fibers

Figure 95. Developing periodontal membrane. ×160.

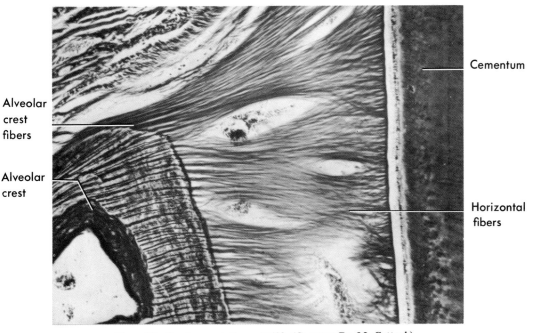

Cementum

Alveolar
crest
fibers

Alveolar
crest

Horizontal
fibers

Figure 96. Alveolar crest fibers. ×420. (Courtesy Dr. M. Cattoni.)

Figure 97.   Proceeding rootward in a study of the periodontal space one encounters another group of fibers which are arranged for the most part in a horizontal position and are accordingly known as the *horizontal fibers*. Another group of fibers observed in a mesiodistal section of the cervical region of two adjacent teeth arise in the region of the root apical to the cemento-enamel junction, pass over the alveolar crest, and terminate in the same part of the adjacent tooth. These fibers are known as the transeptal fibers (Fig. 107).

Figure 98.   The remainder of the apical part of the periodontal space is occupied by a fourth group which are arranged in an oblique manner. They are known as the *oblique* fibers. Still another group, the apical fibers, originate in the apex of the tooth and are irregularly or radially arranged in reference to the surrounding alveolus.

164

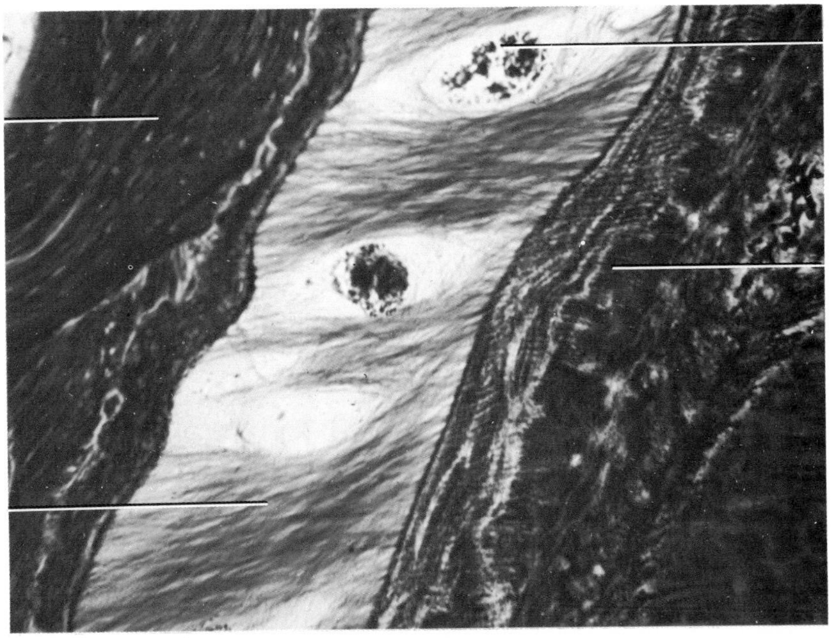

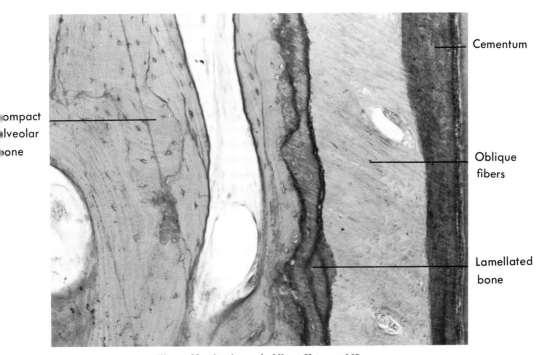

Figure 97. Horizontal fibers. × 420. (Courtesy Dr. M. Cattoni.)

Figure 98. Alveolus and oblique fibers. × 160.

165

Figure 99. In addition to the five groups of fibers mentioned in the preceding paragraphs the periodontal space contains isolated islands of interstitial connective tissue, in which are located the vessels and nerves supplying the periodontal membrane. In addition a group of cells which will be referred to later, the cementoblasts, occupy a position in the periodontal space adjacent to the cementum.

Figure 100. Section of interstitial connective tissue in the periodontal membrane. Note presence of blood and lymph vessels, and also nerve fibers penetrating this area.

166

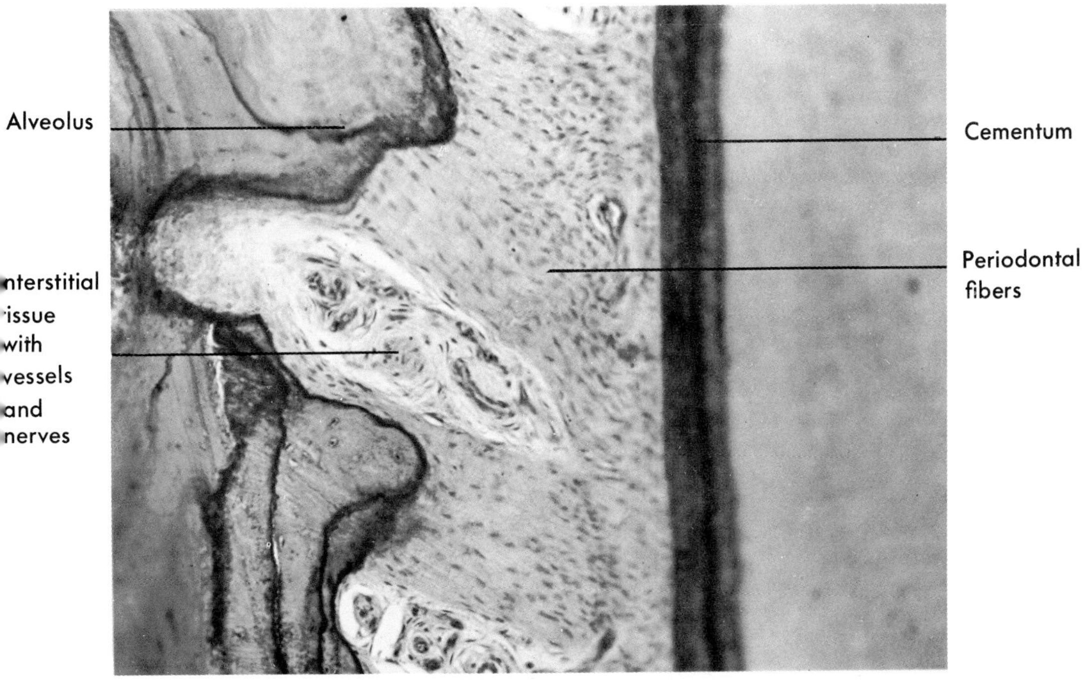

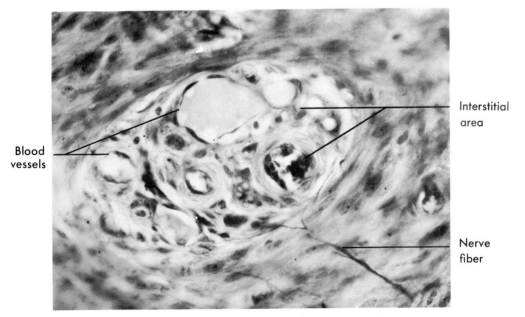

Alveolus

Interstitial tissue with vessels and nerves

Cementum

Periodontal fibers

Figure 99. Alveolus and interstitial tissue. ×160.

Blood vessels

Interstitial area

Nerve fiber

Figure 100. Interstitial tissue. (Courtesy Dr. Sol Bernick.)

167

Figure 101. During the development and eruption of the teeth, remnants of Hertwig's epithelial sheath frequently are not absorbed and remain in the periodontal space. These epithelial remnants appear as strands or nests of cells and are known as the epithelial rests of Malassez.

Figure 102. The vessels of the periodontal membrane are of various calibers. The photograph illustrates a small blood vessel in close proximity to a lymph capillary.

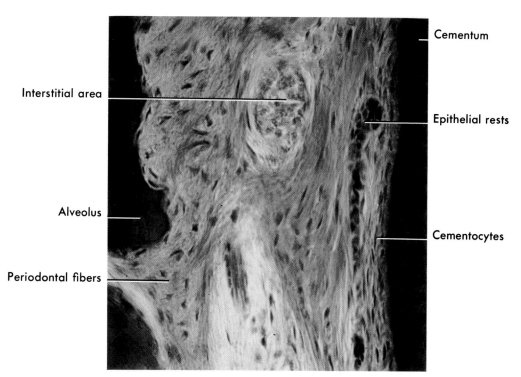

Cementum

Interstitial area

Epithelial rests

Alveolus

Cementocytes

Periodontal fibers

Figure 101. Epithelial rests. ×420.

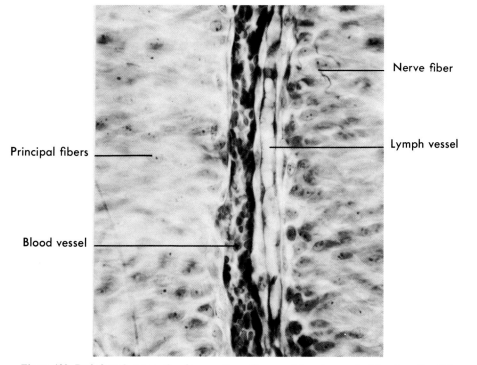

Nerve fiber

Lymph vessel

Principal fibers

Blood vessel

Figure 102. Periodontal space showing small capillary and lymph vessel. (Courtesy Dr. Sol Bernick.)

Figure 103. The distribution of nerve fibers of the periodontal membrane is roughly equivalent to that of the blood vessels. These fibers are derived from the periapical region and the alveolus. The nerves are of three kinds: medullated, nonmedullated, and mixed. The fibers undergo branching and terminate on the surface of the cementum, in the alveolus, and in the structures in the interstitial tissue.

Figure 104. The nature of the nerve terminations in the periodontal membrane has been controversial for some time. The most recent evidence in regard to these structures indicates, as shown here, that the fibers end in loops which may show a beaded structure.

170

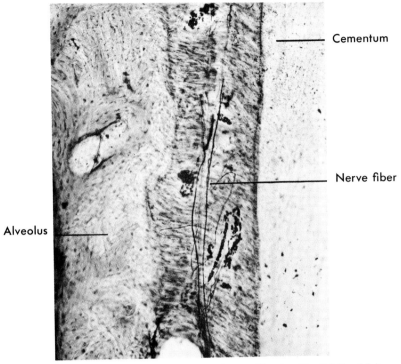

Figure 103. Nerve fibers in periodontal membrane. (Courtesy Dr. Sol Bernick.)

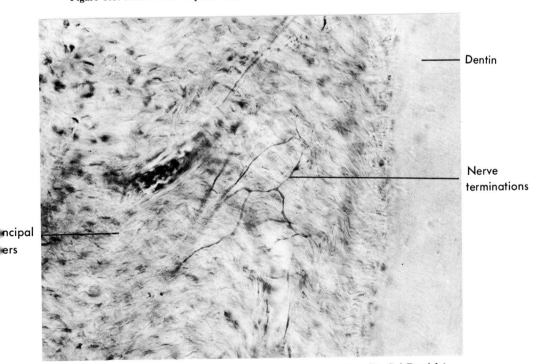

Figure 104. Nerve terminations in periodontal membrane. (Courtesy Dr. Sol Bernick.)

Figure 105. It was previously mentioned that the periodontal membrane was made up for the most part of the collagen fibers. This electron micrograph illustrates in detail the fine structure of a small part of this membrane. Shown in the micrograph are portions of two fibroblasts, *f,* the cell found in greatest numbers in this area, and also bundles of collagen fibers, *col.,* densely arranged in various directions; *n,* nucleus of fibroblast.

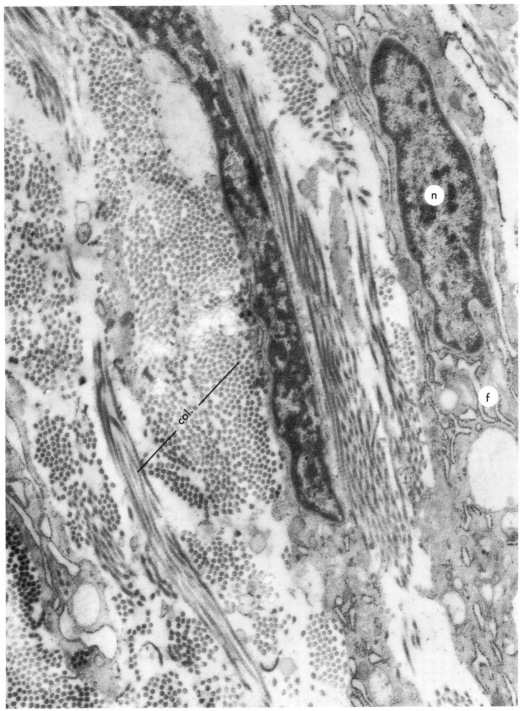

Figure 105. Electron micrograph of periodontal space. ×17,000.

Figure 106. The periodontal fibers are inserted into the surface of the alveolus on one side and in the cementum, *c*, on the tooth surface. This electron micrograph illustrates the manner in which the fibers, *col.*, are inserted into the cementum.

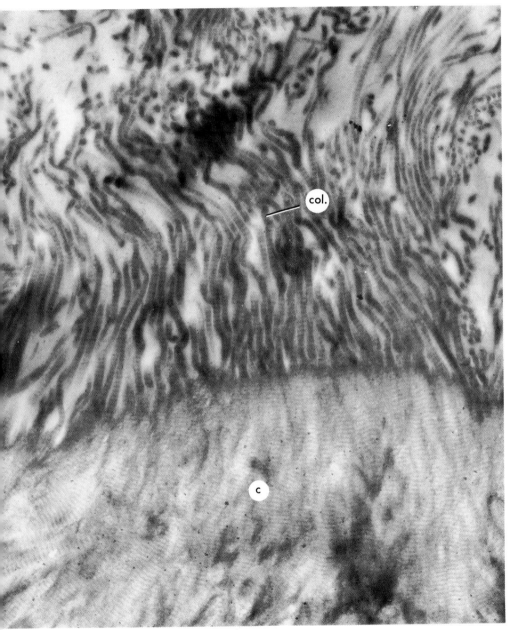

Figure 106. Electron micrograph illustrating insertion of fibers into cementum. ×20,000.

THE ALVEOLUS

Figure 107.   The alveolus is the bony outer surface of the socket, the space normally occupied by the tooth. It is actually part of the jaw and varies in extent as one proceeds from the anterior region, where the jaw itself is a thin bony plate, to the posterior region, where the jaw is much more extensive. The alveolus, also known as the lamina dura, surrounds the root of the tooth and terminates in the region slightly apical to the cemento-enamel junction. The alveolus proper consists of dense bone. Frequently, the surface adjacent to the root, which is subject to resorption and rebuilding, is arranged in parallel lamellae exhibiting several cement lines. Other parts of the alveolus consist for the most part of typical compact bone. Frequently, the alveoli are discontinuous, affording the passage of vessels and nerves from the surrounding area to the periodontal space. In this condition the alveolus is known as the cribriform plate.

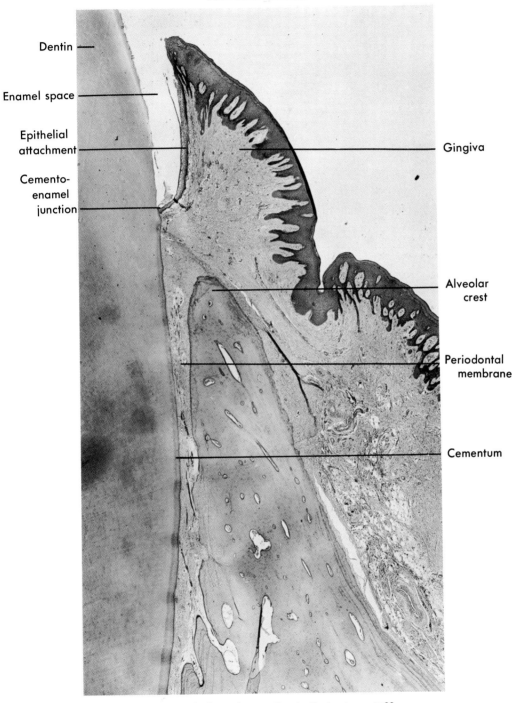

Dentin

Enamel space

Epithelial
attachment

Cemento-
enamel
junction

Gingiva

Alveolar
crest

Periodontal
membrane

Cementum

Figure 107. Gingiva and supporting tooth structures. ×22.

177

Figure 108. It was previously stated that the alveolus differs in its extent in different parts of the jaw and also in the labial and lingual aspects. Shown here is a section of the jaw and tooth in the region of an upper incisor. Examination of this figure shows that the labial alveolus cannot be differentiated from the jaw itself. Further, it is relatively thin. The lingual aspect, however, presents a different situation and consists of one in which one observes a thin lamina dura, which lies adjacent to an extensive system of supporting bony trabeculae. Note that the bony support on the labial surface consists of a thin plate of dense bone.

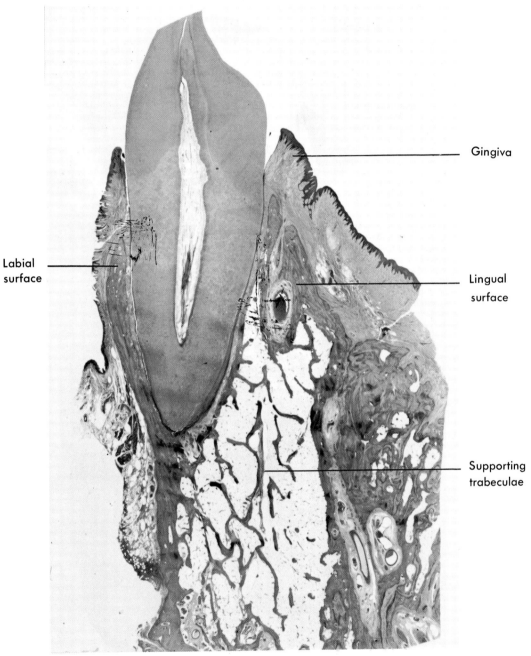

Gingiva

Labial
surface

Lingual
surface

Supporting
trabeculae

Figure 108. Tooth and supporting structures (labiolingual section). ×6.

179

Figure 109. Retrogressive changes for various reasons occur in the supporting structures of the tooth as elsewhere. This mesiodistal section of two lower centrals shows a well formed lamina dura, but the supporting trabeculae of spongy bone have become attenuated.

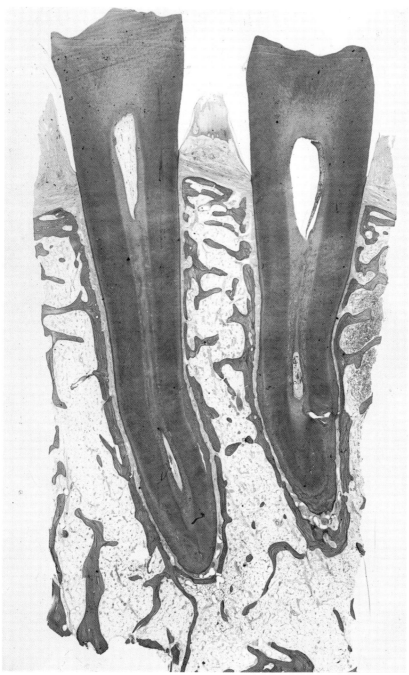

Figure 109. Mesiodistal section of lower incisors. ×9.

Figure 110. In a normal situation the supporting trabeculae are extensive and arranged in such a fashion that they offer a strong support for the tooth. The amount of this tissue varies, as mentioned, in different areas of the jaw. This is well illustrated by comparing Figure 110 with Figure 109. This decalcified mesiodistal section of upper premolars shows the amount and character of the bone support between the roots.

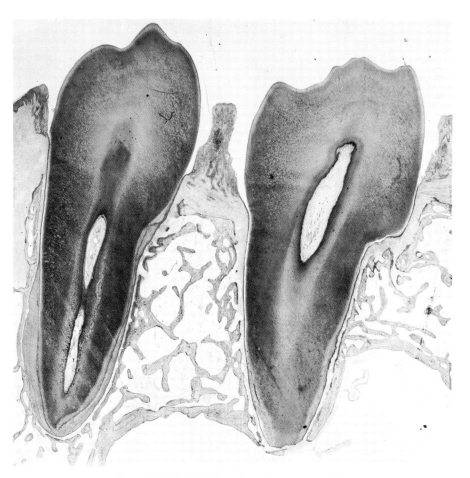

Figure 110. Mesiodistal section of premolars. ×7.

Figure 111. In addition to the supporting trabeculae found between the alveolus and the outer plate of the jaw, there is also an extensive array of trabeculae present between the roots of multirooted teeth. Shown here is a section of the mandible at the level of the root of the molar showing relation of bone supporting structures to the tooth.

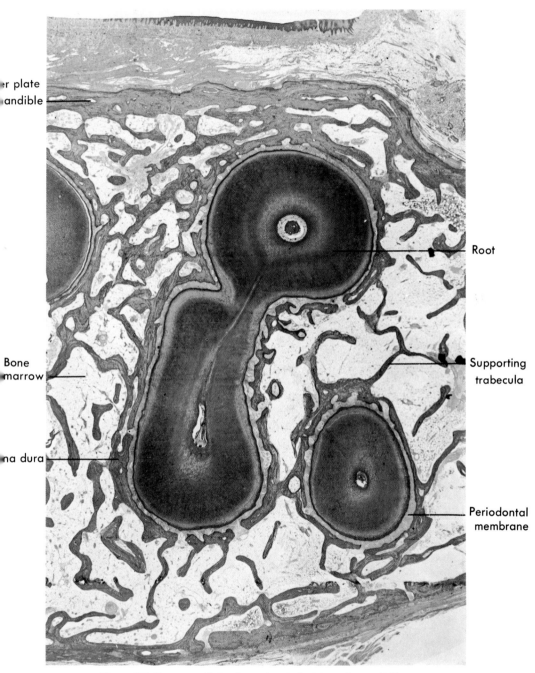

er plate
andible

Root

Bone
marrow

Supporting
trabecula

na dura

Periodontal
membrane

Figure 111. Structure of alveolus and periodontal membrane. ×16.

185

Figure 112. The surface of the alveoli adjacent to the tooth may present diverse appearances depending upon conditions related to eruption, drift, or repositioning of the tooth. In the quiescent state the surface of the bone appears relatively smooth. The difference in the appearance and direction of the lamellae, however, strongly suggest that a refabrication of the alveolus has taken place. The fibers of the periodontal membrane are arranged, for the most part, in a slightly oblique direction.

Figure 113. The alveolar crest is illustrated with a portion of the alveolus undergoing resorption by osteoclastic activity. The condition is quite common and the etiology is often unknown.

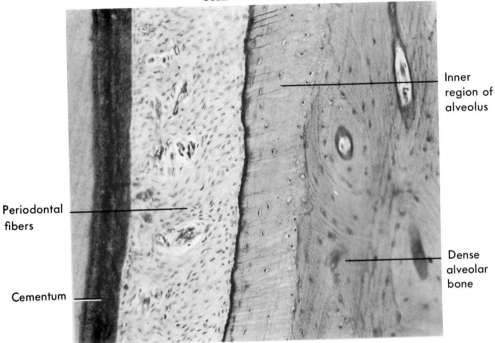

Inner region of alveolus

Periodontal fibers

Cementum

Dense alveolar bone

Figure 112. Alveolar crest. × 160.

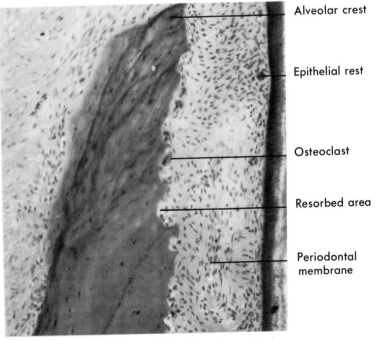

Alveolar crest

Epithelial rest

Osteoclast

Resorbed area

Periodontal membrane

Figure 113. Alveolus and periodontal membrane. × 160.

187

Figure 114. A variation in the structure and appearance of the alveolus from that shown in Figure 113 is illustrated. The jagged edges on the inner surface indicate some previous resorption. The surface, however, does not indicate subsequent rebuilding. Although compact in nature, Haversian systems are not evident.

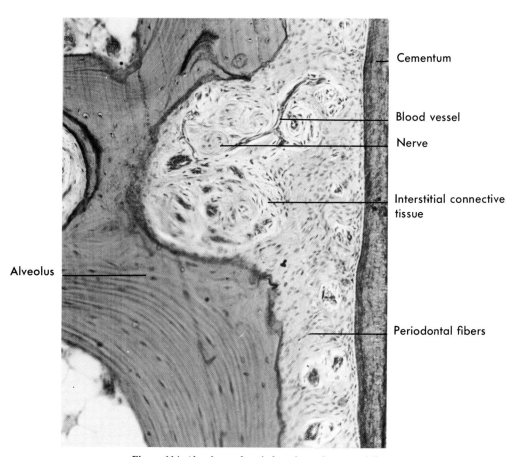

Cementum

Blood vessel

Nerve

Interstitial connective tissue

Alveolus

Periodontal fibers

Figure 114. Alveolus and periodontal membrane. × 160.

DEVELOPMENT OF GINGIVA

Figure 115. The gingivae are formed at the time the tooth erupts and protrudes through the oral epithelium. They consist of modified oral epithelium and surround the cervical part of the tooth.

The manner in which the gingiva form may be understood from a study of Figures 115 to 118. The first of these is a photomicrograph of a developing tooth which is in the late pre-eruption stage. It will be noted that the crown of the tooth has already reached the lower part of the oral epithelium.

190

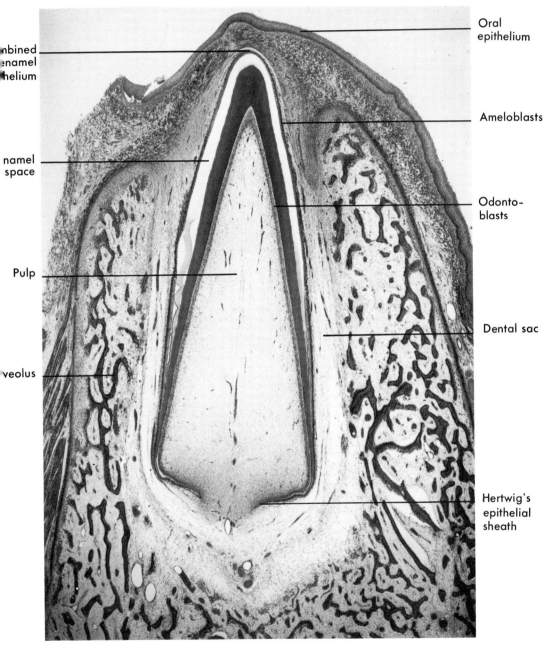

Oral epithelium

Combined enamel epithelium

Enamel space

Pulp

Alveolus

Ameloblasts

Odonto-blasts

Dental sac

Hertwig's epithelial sheath

Figure 115. Late pre-eruptive stage of tooth development. × 23.

191

Figure 116. In a later stage of development, the crown is now protruding into the oral cavity although not as yet exposed to the oral environment. A series of interesting and important changes are taking place at this time which are more clearly shown in Figure 117.

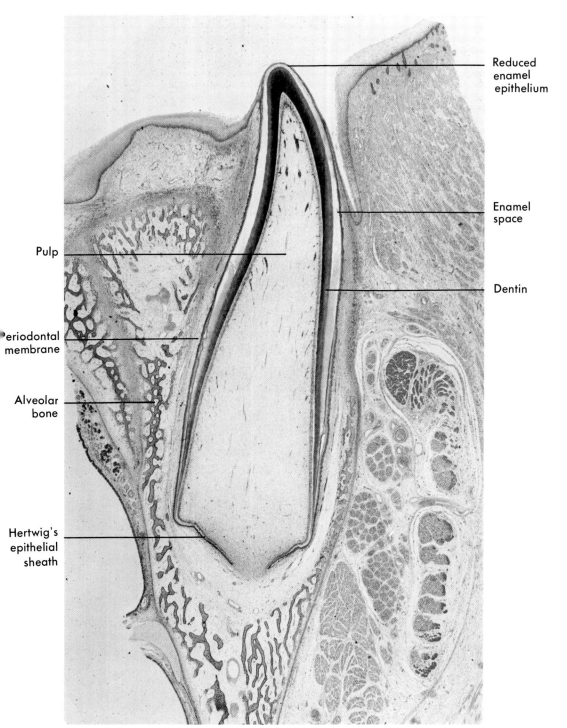

Reduced
enamel
epithelium

Enamel
space

Dentin

Pulp

Periodontal
membrane

Alveolar
bone

Hertwig's
epithelial
sheath

Figure 116. Beginning of eruption. ×18.

Figure 117. This photomicrograph shows in detail a high magnification of part of the specimen illustrated in Figure 116. At the coronal region one may observe the combined enamel epithelium and below this remnants of the partially demineralized enamel. In a somewhat more apical region one may observe on the periphery of the enamel an attenuated layer of ameloblasts and external to them a stratified layer of epithelium, the stratum intermedium. It will be noted that these cells have joined with the oral epithelium in a coronal aspect. Accordingly, in this stage of eruption the stratum intermedium, heretofore quiescent, begins to proliferate and forms a union with the oral epithelium. Further differentiation of the oral epithelium and eruption give rise to the modified tissue known as the gingivae. The stratum intermedium continues to proliferate, and by the time the tooth erupts, it is applied to the surface of the enamel and extends rootward as far as the cemento-enamel junction as the epithelial attachment.

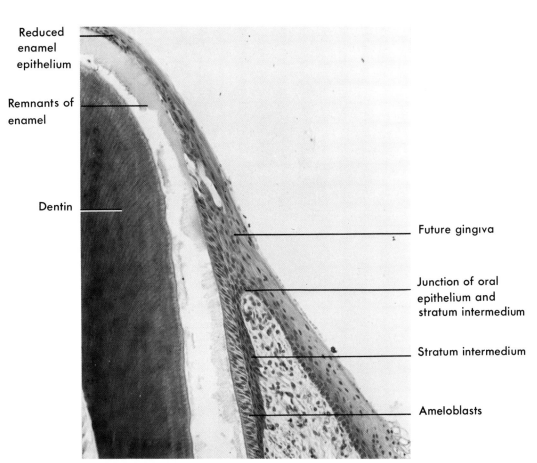

Reduced
enamel
epithelium

Remnants of
enamel

Dentin

Future gingiva

Junction of oral
epithelium and
stratum intermedium

Stratum intermedium

Ameloblasts

Figure 117. Detail of crown of tooth at beginning of eruption. ×400.

STRUCTURE OF GINGIVA

Figure 118. This labiolingual section of the gingiva shows that the surface is invested with a stratified squamous epithelium thrown into deep pegs. Approximately 1 to 1.5 mm rootward of the crest of the gingiva there is a pronounced groove or sulcus which marks the level of muco-gingival mucosa. The epithelium rests upon a basement membrane and is supported by a fibrous tunica propria containing a few scattered elastic fibers. The epithelium of the crest of the gingiva continues on the surface of the enamel as far as the cemento-enamel junction. This tissue, the epithelial attachment, is thinner than the gingival epithelium and does not exhibit the pegs found in the former. A structural feature not readily shown in the type of section used to illustrate this figure is the gingival sulcus, normally a capillary space which extends from the gingival crest apically for 1 mm or less. It is bounded on one side by the inner surface of the epithelial attachment and on the other by the outer surface of the enamel.

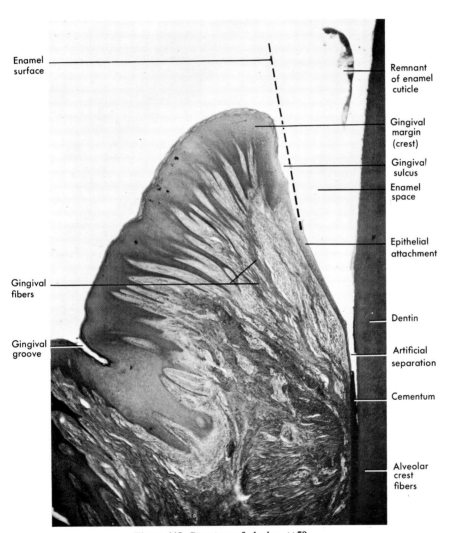

Enamel surface

Remnant of enamel cuticle

Gingival margin (crest)

Gingival sulcus

Enamel space

Epithelial attachment

Gingival fibers

Dentin

Artificial separation

Gingival groove

Cementum

Alveolar crest fibers

Figure 118. Structure of gingiva. ×50.

Figure 119. When the gingivae are viewed from a frontal view or cut in a mesiodistal direction, they present the appearance shown in this figure and are known as the interdental papillae. Examination of this figure reinforces most of the histologic description which is applicable to a labiolingual section. Other structures of interest shown are the transseptal fibers of the periodontal membrane and the alveolar crest.

Figure 120. A section of a portion of the epithelial attachment at relatively high magnification shows that this strip of epithelium may be quite extensive in nature. It normally terminates at the cemento-enamel junction and exhibits a cuticle on the surface adjacent to the enamel.

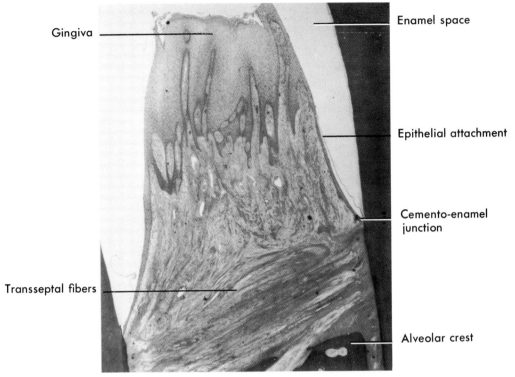

Gingiva

Enamel space

Epithelial attachment

Cemento-enamel junction

Transseptal fibers

Alveolar crest

Figure 119. Interdental papilla. × 160.

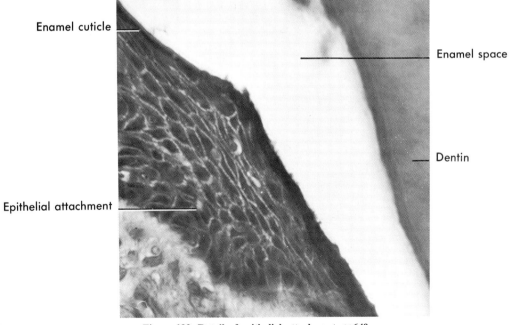

Enamel cuticle

Enamel space

Dentin

Epithelial attachment

Figure 120. Detail of epithelial attachment. × 640.

GINGIVAL MUCOSA

Figure 121. The gingival mucosa consists of a layer of thick stratified squamous epithelium, the base of which is thrown into folds known as rete pegs. The epithelium rests upon a basement membrane and subjacent to this a loosely arranged lamina propria of collagenous and a few elastic fibers. The epithelium undergoes functional changes from time to time, especially in the character of the surface layers and in the number and depth of the pegs. Shown here is a portion of the gingival mucosa in which the surface layers are relatively unchanged.

Figure 122. This section of gingival mucosa appears thinner than the specimen illustrated in Figure 121 and exhibits a mild degree of keratinization of the surface layers.

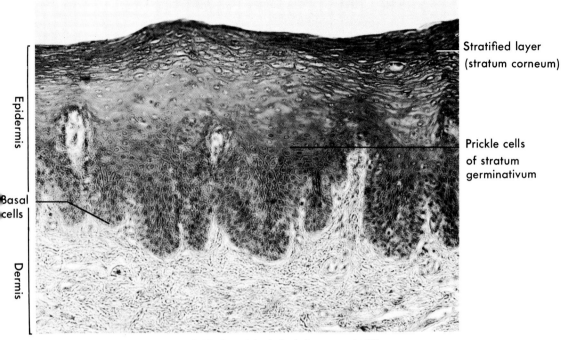

Stratified layer
(stratum corneum)

Epidermis

Prickle cells
of stratum
germinativum

Basal
cells

Dermis

Figure 121. Nonkeratinized gingival mucosa. ×400.

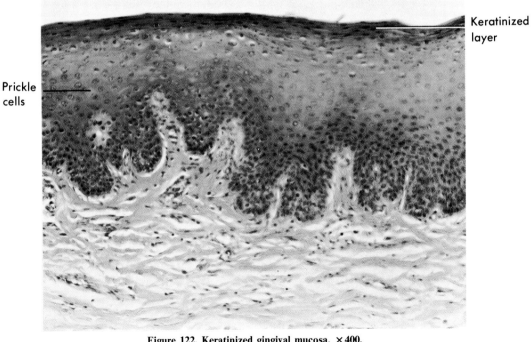

Keratinized
layer

Prickle
cells

Figure 122. Keratinized gingival mucosa. ×400.

14

Figure 123. The section of gingival mucosa in this photomicrograph differs from the two specimens previously shown in that the epithelial pegs are more pronounced and the keratinized surface is well defined.

Figure 124. This section shows a strip of epithelium of a capuchin monkey. It can be observed that this mucosa is similar in structure to the human gingival mucosa shown in the three preceding figures. This is a two micron section and the cells appear somewhat more compactly arranged than those observed in thicker light sections of the human gingival mucosa. Layers of mucosa shown in subsequent electron micrographs are indicated by 1, 2, and 3.

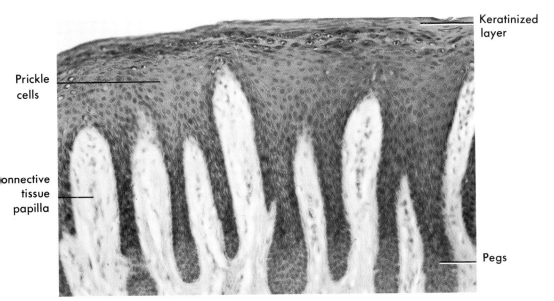

Keratinized layer

Prickle cells

Connective tissue papilla

Pegs

Figure 123. Gingival mucosa exhibiting extensive pegs. ×420.

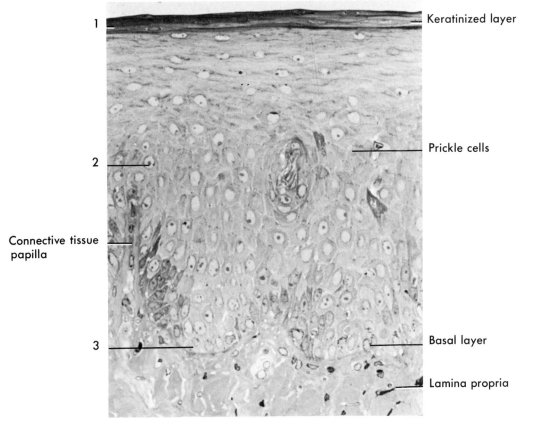

1

Keratinized layer

2

Prickle cells

Connective tissue papilla

3

Basal layer

Lamina propria

Figure 124. Gingival mucosa (capuchin). ×640.

Figure 125. This electron micrograph and those shown in Figures 121 and 122 are illustrations of the gingival mucosa of the capuchin monkey shown in Figure 124 and photographed at three different levels indicated by the numerals 1, 2, and 3 in the optical photograph.

This micrograph (level 1) illustrates the detailed structure of the keratinized surface layer which shows a nucleus, n, of a cell undergoing this process. Below the dark surface layer are several cells, n_2, which are elongated and are in a state preparatory to becoming keratinized.

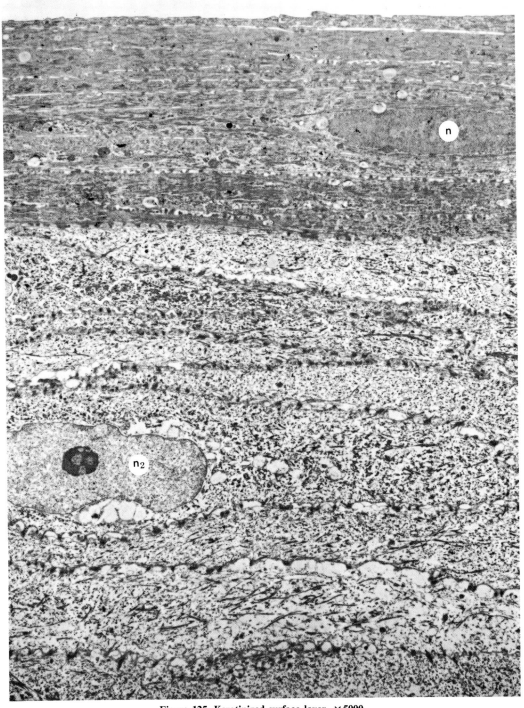

Figure 125. Keratinized surface layer. ×5000.

Figure 126. The cells located above the basal layer exhibiting intercellular bridges are called prickle cells (level 2 in Figure 124). The micrograph shows the detailed structure of one of these cells. The intercellular bridges are shown to consist in part of cell junctions known as desmosomes, *d*. The tonofilaments, *t,* of adjacent cells attach to the desmosomes at the cell junction.

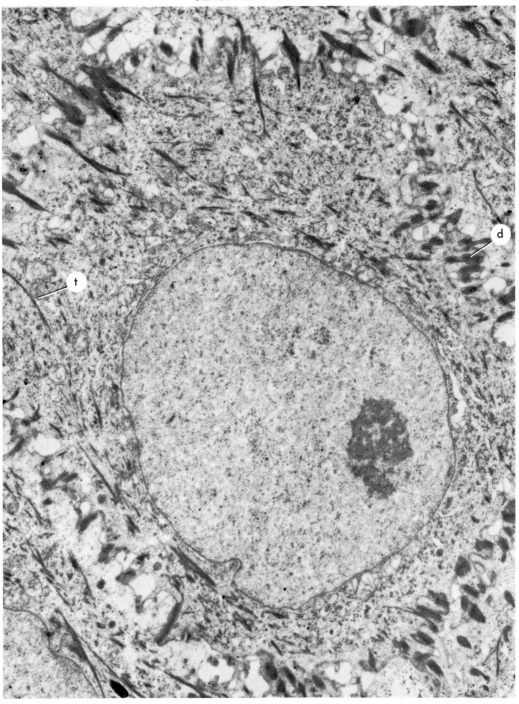

Figure 126. Prickle cell layer. ×11,000.

Figure 127. The basal cells, *b.c.,* shown in this electron micrograph rest upon a well defined basement membrane, *b.m.* (level 3 in Figure 124). This specimen, unlike the human specimen, may contain several pigment granules, *p.* The basal cells are attached to the basement membrane by specialized cell junctions known as hemi-desmosomes; *p,* prickle cell.

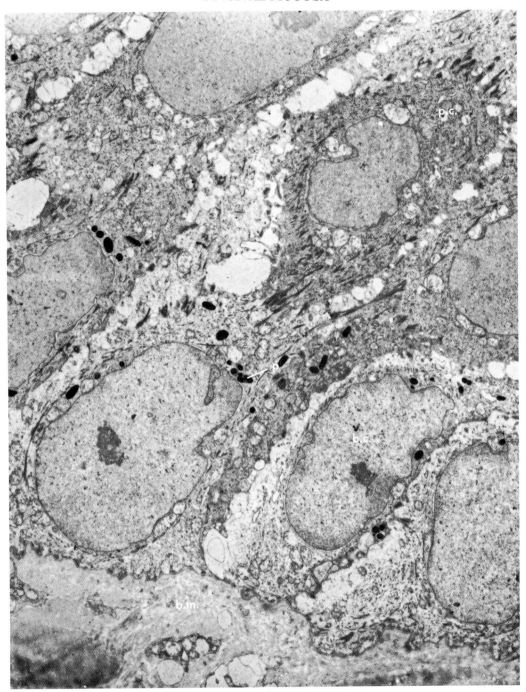

Figure 127. Basal layer and basement membrane. ×4,900.

Figure 128. The mucous membrane of the lip is of interest since it exhibits several modifications in different areas. The labial surface of the lip is invested with an epithelium characteristic of the oral cavity, the area exposed to the environment becomes thinner, vessels are in intimate association with it, and it also undergoes keratinization. It is known as the red area of the lip. The remainder of the surface epithelium is typical of skin in other parts of the body and contains hair follicles, and sebaceous and sweat glands.

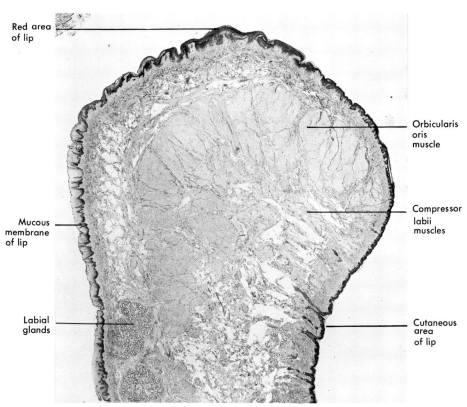

Red area
of lip

Orbicularis
oris
muscle

Mucous
membrane
of lip

Compressor
labii
muscles

Labial
glands

Cutaneous
area
of lip

Figure 128. Vertical section of the lip. × 12.

211

8 ERUPTION and SHEDDING

Figure 129. A vertical section of part of the jaw of a newborn shows the position and structural features of the lip and tongue, a permanent and deciduous anterior tooth and adnexa prior to eruption, and also the vestibule, the derivative of the embryonic lip band furrow. Inferior to the lingual sulcus one may observe portions of the sublingual duct and gland.

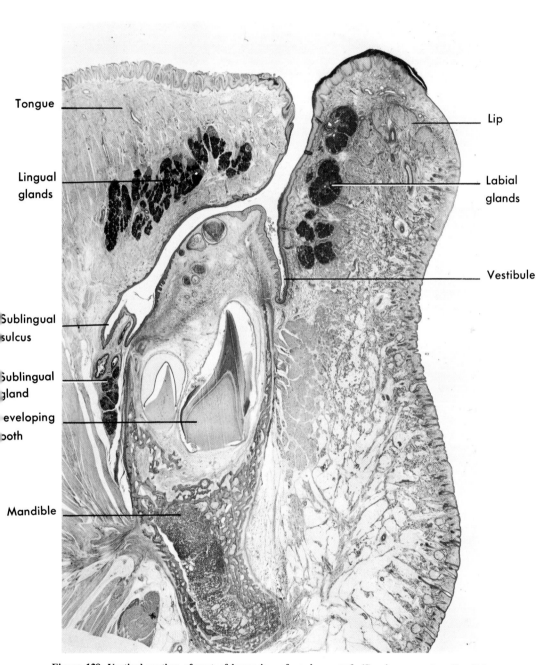

Tongue

Lingual
glands

Sublingual
sulcus

Sublingual
gland

Developing
tooth

Mandible

Lip

Labial
glands

Vestibule

Figure 129. Vertical section of part of lower jaw of newborn. ×6. (Specimen courtesy Dr. Sol Bernick.)

213

Figure 130. This is a microphotograph of a portion of the mandible removed from the molar region of a young rhesus monkey in which mixed dentition was present. The tooth on the left is a permanent molar. To the right the two erupted teeth have undergone root resorption and the crowns of the succedaneous teeth are in close proximity to the reabsorbed root surfaces. The deciduous teeth are ready to exfoliate.

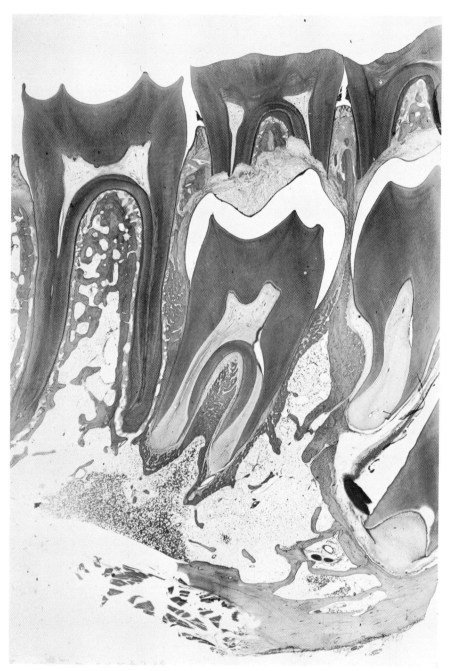

Figure 130. Section of molar region of rhesus showing resorption of deciduous teeth. ×7.5.

Figure 131. The resorption of the roots which occurs in connection with shedding is brought about chiefly as a result of osteoclastic activity.

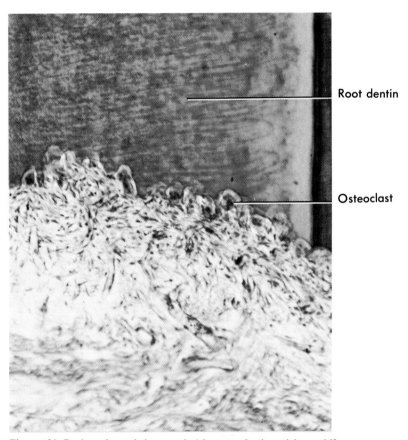

Root dentin

Osteoclast

Figure 131. Region of root being resorbed by osteoclastic activity. × 160.

217

Figure 132. Posterior permanent teeth are often impacted and fail to erupt. This is usually due to a malpositioning of the affected tooth. An impacted molar is shown in relation to an adjacent tooth. These teeth may retain their vitality or may undergo regressive changes. The intimate relation of the crown of these teeth to the root of the adjacent tooth usually results in resorption of the normal tooth and bone with which it makes contact.

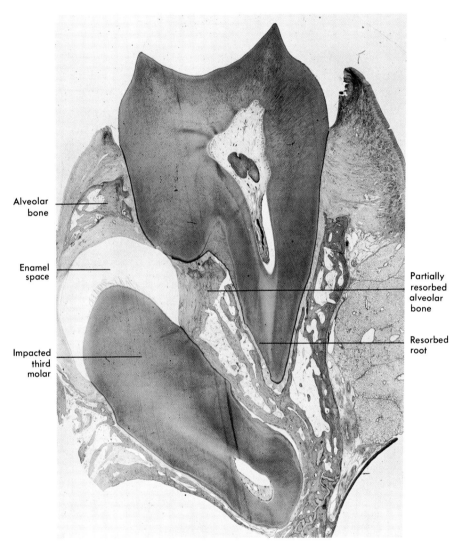

Alveolar
bone

Enamel
space

Impacted
third
molar

Partially
resorbed
alveolar
bone

Resorbed
root

Figure 132. Impacted tooth and root resorption. × 7.5.

219

Figure 133. Posterior teeth located in the region of the maxillary sinus are often positioned in such a manner that the roots are in close proximity to, or actually impinge upon, the floor of the sinus and may be in intimate association with the layer of epithelial cells known as the Schneiderian membrane. Manipulation of teeth in this area requires careful consideration of the anatomic relationship of the teeth and surrounding structures.

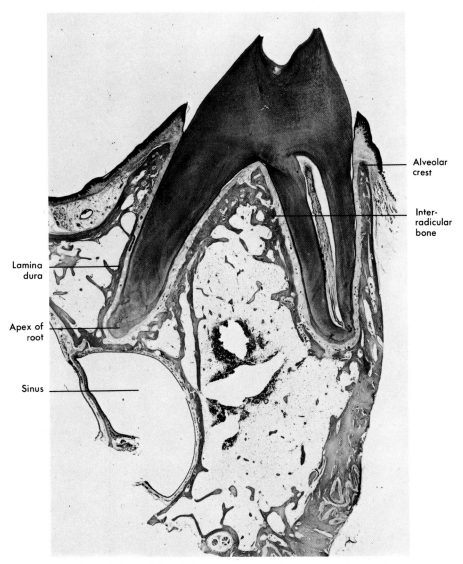

Figure 133. Tooth in relation to the floor of the maxillary sinus. ×8.

221

9 PALATE

Figure 134. The mucosa of the hard palate resembles that of the gingiva. A lamina propria is present except in the area of the midline and the gingivae. The fibers of the submucosa consist of heavy bundles of collagen fibers arranged vertically and are firmly attached to the periosteum of the hard palate. The submucosa of the anterior one-third of the hard palate contains a large amount of adipose tissue and is known as the fatty zone. In the posterior two-thirds of the submucosa the adipose tissue is replaced by mucous glands and is known as the glandular zone. Epithelial pearls, consisting of aggregates of modified epithelial cells, often occur in the midline region. They are remnants of cells that were present at the time of fusion of the two halves of the palate.

PALATE

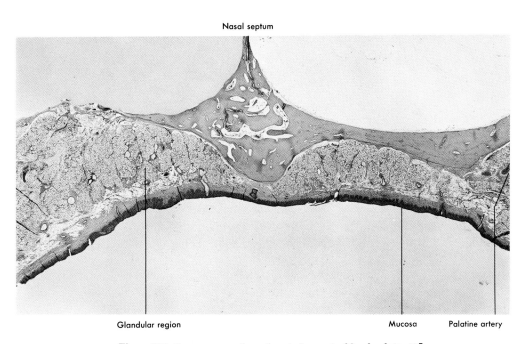

Nasal septum

Glandular region　　　　　　　　　　　Mucosa　　　Palatine artery

Figure 134. Transverse section of posterior part of hard palate. ×5.

Figure 135.   This section of the mucosa of the posterior region of the hard palate shows that it is invested with a layer of stratified squamous epithelium thrown into deep folds. The basement membrane (not shown) is contiguous with a stout lamina propria. Subjacent to the lamina propria one may observe a considerable area occupied by mucous glands.

Figure 136.   The longitudinal section of the entire palate is included here for purposes of orientation. It shows the extent of the palate occupied by the mucosa and the relatively large area occupied by the submucosa. Also shown is the posterior continuation of the musculotendinous soft palate.

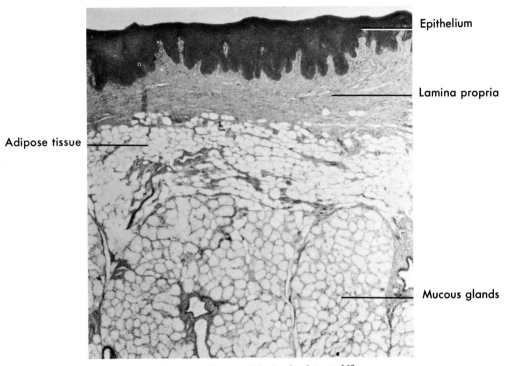

Epithelium

Lamina propria

Adipose tissue

Mucous glands

Figure 135. Mucosa of the hard palate. × 160.

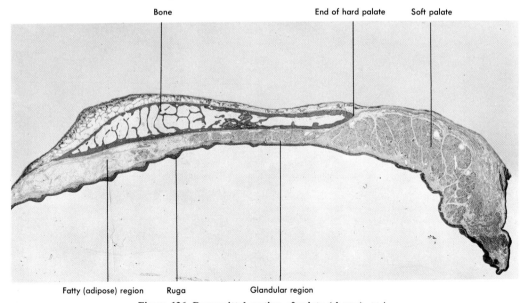

Bone

End of hard palate

Soft palate

Fatty (adipose) region

Ruga

Glandular region

Figure 136. Parasagittal section of palate (rhesus). × 4.

225

PALATE

Figure 137. The photograph shows the structure of the human soft palate. The central area is made up, for the most part, of muscle. The mucosa of the oral surface is similar to other parts of the oral cavity and exhibits a thick glandular submucosa. The termination is thrown into delicate finger-like projections. At this point the epithelium changes to one resembling the nasal mucosa. The glands that are present in the thick submucosa of the pharyngeal surface of the soft palate are of the seromucous type.

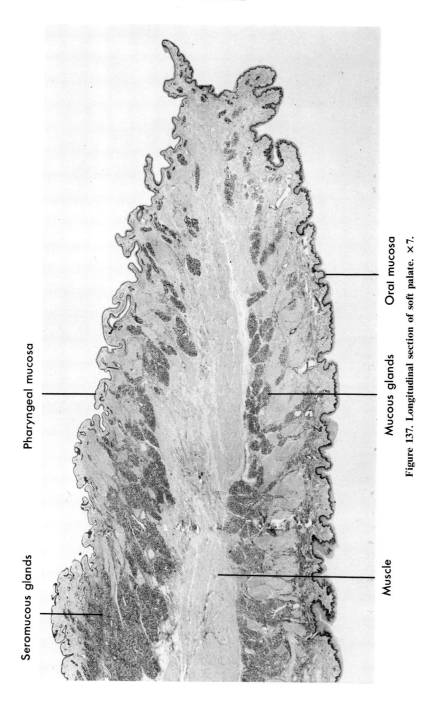

Pharyngeal mucosa

Seromucous glands

Oral mucosa

Mucous glands

Muscle

Figure 137. Longitudinal section of soft palate. ×7.

227

Figure 138. This microphotograph illustrates the mucosa and submucosa of the oral surface of the soft palate. The numerous glands with their ducts are shown in relation to the mucosa.

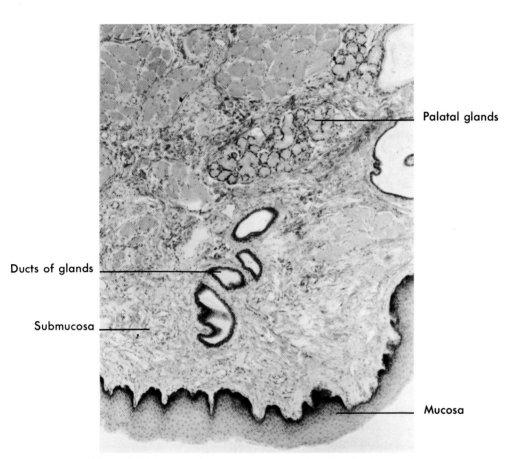

Figure 138. Mucosa and submucosa of oral surface of soft palate. × 60.

Figure 139. This microphotograph illustrates the detailed structure of the mucosa of the oral surface of the soft palate. It consists of a nonkeratinized stratified squamous epithelium only moderately folded at its base. Also shown are the ducts of the mucous glands located in the submucosa. This mucosa is similar to that found in most of the areas of the oral cavity.

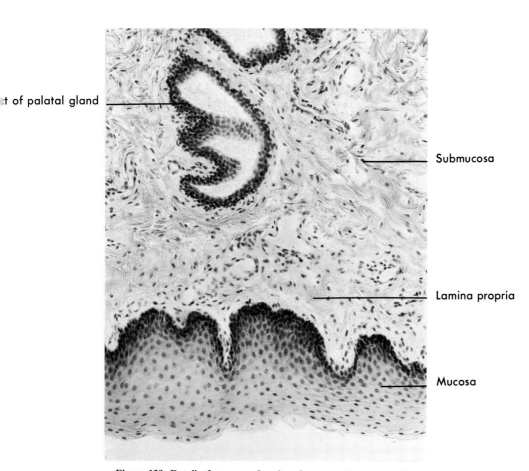

t of palatal gland

Submucosa

Lamina propria

Mucosa

Figure 139. Detail of mucosa of oral surface of soft palate. ×420.

Figure 140. The submucosa of the oral surface of the soft palate contains numerous mucous glands. An example of the glands that occur in this region is shown.

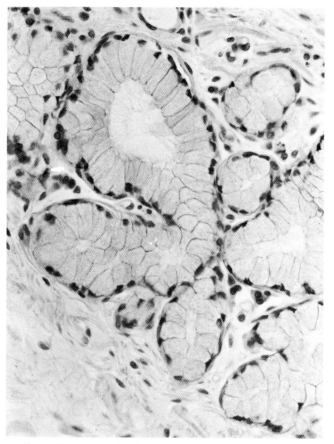

Figure 140. Mucous glands in submucosa of soft palate. ×640.

10 TEMPOROMANDIBULAR JOINT

Figure 141. The temporomandibular joint is a diarthrosis which permits movement of the mandible. The important structures making up the joint are the head of the condyle, an articular disc, and the mandibular fossa and articular tubercle of the temporal bone.

The head of the condyle is covered with a thick layer of fibrous connective tissue and occupies a position in the resting state below (inferior to) the mandibular fossa. Between the bony fossa of the temporal bone and the head of the condyle one may observe an extremely thick articular disc, which in the section illustrated is roughly s-shaped. This disc is composed of fibrocartilage and is thickest in the region of the fossa. The surface of the temporal bone in this region is also invested with fibrocartilage. Superior to the head of the condyle and inferior to the mandibular fossa one may observe spaces which separate the articular disc from these structures. They are known as the inferior and superior articular spaces respectively.

234

Mandibular
fossa

Articular
disc

Fibrous
covering

Mandibular
condyle

Articular
space

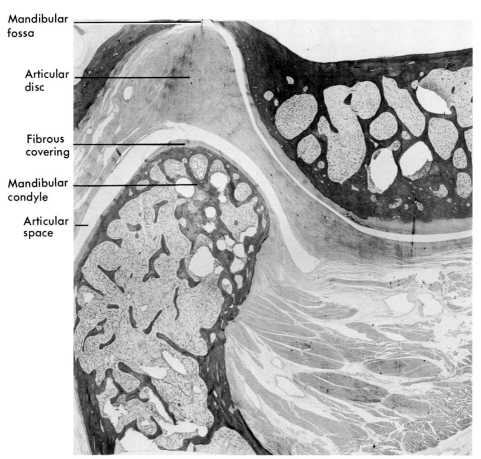

Figure 141. Temporomandibular joint. × 10.

235

INDEX

238

240